THE
DOLOMITES
MOUNTAINS OF CORAL

Origins, History, Natural Attractions

Text by
Andrea Innocenti

Geological Sections by
Michele Cecchi

BONECHI

LEIMGRUBER

Contents

Distributed by:

LEIMGRUBER
Via Nazionale/Nationalstr., 58 - 39040 Ora/Auer (BZ)
Tel. 0471/81 09 92 - 81 15 29 - Fax 0471/81 06 02
e-mail: arthur_leimgruber@rolmail.net

Publication created and designed by:
Casa Editrice Bonechi
Editorial management: Alberto Andreini
Graphic design and cover: Maria Rosanna Malagrinò
Picture research: Alberto Andreini
Editing: Giovannella Masini
Translation: Paula Boomsliter
Make-up: Vanni Berti
Drawings: Paolo Fiumi
Mountain relief graphics reproduced by permission of Carte Kompass.

Printed in Italy by Centro Stampa Editoriale Bonechi
Sesto Fiorentino - Firenze

PICTURE CREDITS

Andrea Innocenti: *pages 2-3; 5; 6-7 large photograph; 8; 9; 10-11; 12; 14;
15 top; 16; 17; 24 center and right; 28 top, center left, and bottom; 29 top;
30-31 large photograph; 32; 33 bottom; 38; 39; 40-41 large photograph;
42-43; 44; 45 bottom; 46; 47; 48; 49; 50; 51; 52-53; 54; 55; 56-57; 58; 59;
60-61; 62 bottom inset; 64; 65 top and bottom right; 67; 68 left; 71; 72;
73 top; 74 top and center; 75 top; 76 small photographs; 78; 79; 80; 81; 82;
83 bottom; 84; 85 bottom; 87 bottom; 88-89; 90; 91; 92; 93; 94; 95; 96; 97;
98; 99; 100; 101; 102; 104-105; 107 top and bottom right; 108; 109;
110-111; 112 bottom; 114-115 bottom; 115 top; 117 top left; 118 bottom
left; 120 bottom; 121; 122-123; 124 bottom right; 125; 126; 127 left; 128;
129; 130; 132; 134 bottom; 136-137; 138; 139; 140 bottom (left and right);
141; 143; 145; 146; 147; 148; 149; 152; 153 first three photographs from
top; 155 top; 156 center and bottom; 157 right; 158-159.*

Ghigo Roli: *pages 7 small photograph; 13; 18-19; 20-21; 22-23; 24 left; 25;
28 center right; 36-37; 40 small photographs; 45 top; 62-63; 63 top;
65 bottom left; 66; 68-69 large photograph; 70 top; 73 bottom; 74 bottom;
75 bottom; 77-78 large photograph; 83 top; 85 top; 86; 87 top; 103;
106-107 large photograph; 112 top; 113; 114 top; 115 bottom right;
116 top; 119; 120 top; 127 right; 131; 133; 134-135 top; 135; 150-151;
153 bottom; 154 top; 155 bottom; 157 left.*

The other photographs in this book were taken by M. N. Batini, Luigi Di
Giovine, Andrea Fantauzzo, and Paolo Giambone *and are property of the
Casa Editrice Bonechi photographic archives.*

Cover photograph by Ghigo Roli. *The photograph of the glacier on the lower
right is by* Andrea Innocenti.

ISBN 88-476-0331-5

* * *

On pages 2 and 3, a beautiful sunset in the Dolomites, from the Passo Giau.
Above, the effect of chemical dissolution of carbonate rocks by rainwater.

A GEOLOGICAL OVERVIEW

It would be impossible, in a guide to these mountains, not to speak of their geological history, since the peculiar rock formations, the suggestiveness of certain singular forms sculpted in the rock by time and the elements, the sheer abundance and the variety of the fossil remains, and the wealth of minerals all beg explanation and however summary answers to the many questions that even the most harried vacationer is likely to ask. Inevitably, the visitor to these parts comes from the increasingly chaotic cities, and just as inevitably is overwhelmed by the immense silences of the rocky crags of the Dolomite Alps. Used as we are to the rhythms of lifestyles that rarely leave us time to reflect, the risk here is to succumb suffocated by the silence or not to succeed in fully appreciating the miracle that nature is showing us. Aesthetically, it is accessible to everyone, but to understand its deeper, intrinsic significance we must learn a new language: that inscribed in the rock by nature over millions of years. The geological sciences can help us to interpret the signs. It will be, for many of us, a new criterion for observing these natural formations from an unusual viewpoint, a totally different system for understanding the mountain and conceiving of the extreme length of the geologic timeline with respect to the extreme brevity of our lives.

The current name of this portion of the Alpine chain, which still at the beginning of the 20th century went by the name of 'Monti Pallidi', derives from that of the predominant element in its geological makeup: **dolomite rock** or dolostone. This is a type of sedimentary rock formed mainly of the mineral dolomite, which takes its name

In the large photo, the powerful Dolomite successions seen from the Passo Rolle, looking in the direction of the Pale di San Martino. Left, a view of the Forcella Clavazole with the Sasso di Toanella and Rocchetta Alta in the background.

from the French mineralogist Dieudonné-Sylvain-Guy-Tancrede de Gratet de Dolomieu (1750-1801). In the area between Trento and Bolzano, Dolomieu collected samples of rock similar to limestone but that did not react when treated with hydrochloric acid. The samples were later analyzed by Nicolas-Théodore de Saussure, a chemist friend of Dolomieu's, who confirmed that they were not composed of calcium carbonate but rather of calcium magnesium carbonate with alternate

layers of calcium ions being replaced by magnesium: $CaMg(CO_3)_2$, a mineral that was unknown until that time. Saussure proposed naming the new mineral 'dolomite', in honor of his mineralogist friend, and the name was later also attributed to the famous geographical area.

For the geologist, the region of the Dolomite Alps is a sort of open-air laboratory containing practically all of the major types of rock existing on the surface of the earth. There are outcrops of rocks of all three major types: sedimentary, igneous, and metamorphic.

Sedimentary rocks are formed by deposit, in different environments, of materials of different

origin, which following complex chemical and physical processes, called collectively *diagenesis*, are transformed into coherent rock: they may, for example, be the result of the accumulation, on a sea bottom, of detritus derived from the erosion of dry land (for example the sandstones, which derive from solidification of sand) or they may form following the accumulation, again on the sea bottom, of the remains of marine organisms (like some types of calcareous rock), or again be the result of a biological construction (for example, the calcareous rocks of the coral barriers) or of direct precipitation, from water, of certain chemical compounds (for example, halite and gypsum, which form rock salt and rock gypsum, respectively)

Igneous rocks, instead, result from the cooling and crystallization of materials of magmatic origin on the surface of the earth (the volcanic rocks such as porphyry are an example) or deep within it (these are the so-called plutonic rocks, for example granite).

Finally, **metamorphic rocks** are rocky bodies, originally of a sedimentary or magmatic nature, that have undergone more or less radical transformation following greater or lesser variations in temperature or pressure with respect to those of

the environment in which they were originally formed.

Wherever it is carried on, the study of the earth's rocks shows us how the planet is in continual evolution. Ours is a living planet, even under its surface. We may consider the lithosphere (that is, the outermost and most rigid part of the planet) to be 'floating' on a substrate which for purposes of discussion we may consider to be fluid. This surface level, penetrating to a depth of about 100 kilometers, is divided into various *plates*: enormous 'rafts' that shift, the ones with respect to the others, with composite movements on the order of at the most a few centimeters per year. When the plates, which coincide with the continents, move slowly away from each other, an ocean is formed in which enormous quantities of igneous rock are produced along the mid-oceanic ridges. It is in the ocean basins and along their margins that there gradually accumulate sediments of different kinds to depths of thousands of meters. Then, after hundreds of millions of years, the plates move together again, pushed by forces of unimaginable power. The enormous masses of material lying between the plates are compressed and corrugated and rise to form the mountain chains. This activity is accompanied by earthquakes and intense volcanic activity.

This complex cycle, from the opening of an ocean basin to the formation of mountain chains by folding, is called **orogeny**. During the history of the earth, which began about four and one-half billion years ago, many cycles of this type have occurred: in practice, paleo-oceans were formed and closed again various times. The last cycle of orogeny, in chronological order, is the Alpine orogeny. Following the closure of the Sea of Tethys, it gave rise in Eurasia to mountain

The Parco Naturale Fanes-Sennes-Braies. The enormous folds in sedimentary rocks along the slopes of the Sasso della Croce bear mute witness to the immense forces that have shaped these rocks over the course of time.

chains such as the Alps, the Appennines, the Dinaric Alps, the Carpathians, the Taurus and the Zagros chains, and the Himalayas.

The Dolomite Alps, or more simply Dolomites, were also formed during the Alpine orogeny, and their rocks tell its history. They are precious witnesses of past events, photographs of fabulous habitats populated by strange, now-extinct plants and animals. The history goes from about 270 to 130 million years ago and can be read in the deep accumulations of sediments that reach a maximum depth of about 3000 meters.

Underlying the whole Dolomite mass is the so-called Paleozoic metamorphic foundation; in other words, the remains of the highlands created during the earlier Hercynian orogeny. These masses eroded and the materials carried off, in this case mainly pebbles, were deposited in the lower areas. Later, intense **volcanic activity** took place in the western portion of the

The Pale di San Martino. The layers of sedimentary origin are highly contorted as a result of the complex tectonic movements to which they were subjected. Below, the Cimon della Pala, showing Werfen Formation layers in thin stratifications and bright colors.

Dolomite area, and huge quantities of volcanic materials were deposited to enormous depths. Perhaps the best-known of these minerals are the quartziferous porphyries: the cobblestones used in old-style road paving are cut from this rock. In the times between lava flows, sandstones of continental origin were deposited in relatively thin layers. It is in one of these layers that paleontologists found a small terrestrial reptile that inhabited these then sub-desert areas about 270 million years ago.

The sediments above the porphyries, called Gardena Sandstone by the geologists, show that following the demolition of the volcanic structures the region became a flood plain inhabited by reptiles and amphibians. The rivers that cut through the plain flowed into in a sea to the east of the Dolomite area. And the sea, from this moment on, became the leading actor in the geological history of the area. About 260 million years ago, the coastal plain was invaded by the sea as it pushed eastward, mainly because of the slow sinking of the region.

In the beginning, the sea was shallow and subject to frequent changes in level; the intense evaporation gave rise to rocks that are called

evaporites, here represented above all by rock gypsum and rock anhydrite, and grouped by the geologists under the name of the Bellerophon Formation, from the name of an invertebrate fossil found here. Where the sea was deeper, there were deposited a series of calcareous rocks, very dark in color because rich in organic material and with many fossils (mollusks, fish, corals, etc.); in fact, if broken with a hammer, these rocks emit a characteristic bituminous odor.

In this sea, which was still very shallow, there deposited sediments of different kinds (Werfen Formation), generally in close, vivaciously-colored layers, that contain the fossil remains of lamellibranchs, gastropods, and echinoderms and that document the passage from the Paleozoic to the Mesozoic era. Corresponding to this important

The fossil remains of gastropods, lamellibranchs, and echinoderms are clearly visible in the stratifications of the sedimentary rocks.

boundary-line drawn by the geologists, there occurred one of the most catastrophic biological crises in the history of the planet, which brought about the extinction of many species. This global phenomenon is recorded in the rocks of the Dolomite Alps, where the paleontologists have noted a considerable decrease in the variety of fossil species as they move from the layers below to those above the line. Up to that time, over about 30 million years, there was created the substrate on which the Dolomite peaks proper were formed. Later, about 240 million years ago, there occurred a brief period of emersion with consequent erosion of some of the highlands. Then the sea again submerged the region, and sediments of a prevalently calcareous nature were deposited. The **tectonic movements** that caused these events gave the sea bottom an extremely complex morphology made of reliefs and depressions.

An exhibit of fossils at the Museo Paleontologico Rinaldo Zardini at the Ciasa Ra Regoles in Cortina d'Ampezzo.

Above, the Sciliar massif, the rock of which is characterized by Sciliar Dolostone; right, the Sella group, clearly showing the horizontal stratifications of the Dolomia Principale and Cassiana Dolostone, with its typically inclined stratification.

During the periods of emersion, the water was shallow enough to permit the establishment of colonies of organisms such as algae, corals, and sponges capable of fixing the calcium carbonate present in the water and creating small islands, banks, and 'tropical' reefs like those we see today in the Maldives. The slow sinking of the sea bottom, matched by the growth of the colonies, permitted the accumulation of thick layers of these materials of organic origin (Sciliar Dolostone) that may still be observed in many areas of the Dolomite Alps. Initially, the rock was high in $CaCO_3$ sediment or sedimentary rocks, and only later did the process of dolomitization occur. Exactly how it came about is still a subject of discussion among scientists.

Meanwhile, in the deep arms of the sea offshore of the various colonies, there were deposited sediments characteristic of the open sea, as we see from the fossil organisms that have been found in the rock. One of these is the ichthyosaurus, a reptile that lived in the Mesozoic sea and of which some fossil fragments are on display in the Ortisei museum.

These colonies of organisms were eradicated about 230 million years ago, at the beginning of a new phase of intense volcanic activity accompanied by tectonic movements of a certain entity that created two major volcanic landforms in the

THE CORAL MOUNTAINS

*I*t is difficult to imagine that many of the peaks of the Dolomite Alps were once islands far out in the sea, surrounded by **coral reefs** teeming with the most disparate forms of animal and plant life, in an environment similar to that we see today in the 'coral gardens' of the Maldives or many small islands in Polynesia and Melanesia. And yet, coral reefs, or at least their outer portions, represent vast portions of the Rosengarten, the Sciliar, the Latemar, the Marmolada, the Sella, the Pale di San Martino, the Odle group, the Sassolungo, and many other formations in the Dolomites.

Sir Charles Lyell, a 19th-century Scottish geologist, believed that the key to the past lies in the present and that in order to understand what was happening in the Dolomite Alps more than 200 million years ago we should observe that which normally occurs in a coral reef habitat nowadays. We could therefore compare the remote scenario of the Dolomite region with that of a Pacific atoll with a central lagoon, surrounded by a coral reef, that communicates with the ocean through channels in a wall anchored to the sea bottom. The reef is the site of development of organogenic communities constituted by organisms such as corals, algae, and sponges that use the calcium carbonate in sea water to build up their skeletons. When an organism dies, another establishes itself above; thus, with time, there comes to be formed a series of superposed layers that are the main structure of the reef. On the seaward slope there accumulates, es-

pecially during storms, the detritus from the reef as such. The lateral accumulation obviously takes place in inclined layers. In the lagoon, instead, fine sediment, again of a carbonate composition, deposits horizontally.

Among the lagoon, the reef, and the seaward wall there thus exists a certain differentiation as to the type and arrangement of the deposits that accumulate in each site. As the reef grows, the lagoon broadens and the wall expands laterally, giving rise over time to sedimentary structures. Vertical growth is permitted by the slow and progressive subsidence of the ocean floor, with which the vertical growth of the colony must keep pace, since the depth of the water must remain constant if the community is to survive. The maximum depth can be only a few dozen meters, because the reef needs light, a sufficiently high temperature, and good oxygenation of the water.

This situation is similar to that which existed in the Dolomite region 240 and 230 million years ago, during the two reef phases, even though the organisms that existed at the time (which occupied the same ecological niche) were slightly different

from today's. The slow subsidence of the ancient sea bottom and the growth of the colony were therefore the cause of the ample accumulations of the materials that now constitute the backbone of many of the Dolomite area mountains.

The sedimentary structures in the Dolomite massifs, together with much fossil evidence, point to the formation of these mountains in a coral reef habitat; it is easy to observe, for example, both the horizontal stratifications typi-

cal of the lagoonward edge and the inclined stratifications of forereef debris on the seaward slope. And in some cases we can even walk along a submarine 'paleo-reef' - with no need of a diver's outfit!

Above, the Torri del Vaiolet: on the left, the horizontal stratifications typical of the deposits in lagoons protected by reefs; on the right, the inclined stratifications typical of the forereef slope. Center, a diagram of sedimentary rock formation patterns. Left, an atoll in the Maldives, where today's coral reefs are similar to those that existed in the Dolomite region more than 200 million years ago.

The slope of the Sasso Piatto, which coincides perfectly with the original underwater reef face of 230 million years ago. Right, a detail of Dolomia Principale on the Tre Cime of Lavaredo.

region: Predazzo and the Monzoni mountains. There were many secondary vents and intrusions of magma into pre-existing rock, which on account of the high temperature of the magma underwent metamorphism (that is, they were altered by the heat) and as a result became rich in certain newly-formed mineral species. The region was literally submerged by this abundant volcanic production: lava flows, pillow lavas, tufa, cinder and ash, etc. In this manner, as happened at Herculaneum and Pompeii in the first century AD, scenarios dating to 230 million years ago were 'frozen' in the material. The volcanism gradually attenuated and the volcanic landforms began to be slowly demolished by erosion. On that which remained of the original volcanoes there grew up a second generation of organogenic communities largely represented by corals; these deposits originated that which we call Cassiana Dolostone, about 230-220 million years ago. The habitat must have been quite similar to that we now observe on the volcanic islands or the atolls of Polynesia and Melanesia, in which the central cone is surrounded by a coral reef; this formation may later be transformed into an atoll if the volcanic landform sinks and in the meantime the coral colony grows at a rate not less than that of the subsidence. While all this was happening, the deep sea basins around the coral reefs slowly filled with sediments rich in fossil material.

About 225 million years ago, the area again became a coastal area where favorable conditions for the development of these colonies of coralline and algal builders no longer existed, but there were nevertheless deposited series of sediments with characteristic reddish coloration.

Between 225 and 219 million years ago, roughly, the sea again submerged the coastal plain and so created a habitat in all probability quite similar to today's Bahamian tide flats, in which the difference between the high and low tide marks was considerable and there deposited those sediments that now constitute all the rock formations that the geologists have called, collectively, Dolomia Principale and that account for a large part

of the outcrops in the Dolomite region, with a maximum thickness of about 1000 meters. The accumulation of such a thick layer of sediment is naturally due to the phenomenon of slow subsidence of the land that kept pace with the continuous sedimentation. On these coastal plains, when they were not submerged by the sea, there walked various species of dinosaurs who left their tracks (now fossils) in the mud (now solid rock).

At the end of the Triassic period (about 210 million years ago) there occurred a true tectonic subsidence and the Dolomite region sank beneath sea level. The sedimentary rocks that bear witness to events after this time are relatively few, but they

Below, calcareous sediments at the base of the Sasso della Croce, in the Parco Naturale Fanes-Sennes-Braies.

On the following pages, the golden light of sunset on the mountains of the Val Travignolo, near Predazzo, and an evocative sunrise on the craggy peaks of the Pale di San Luciano, seen from the Pale di San Martino.

are in any case rocks formed of sediments deposited in a deep-sea environment.

During the Cenozoic era, more or less 40 million years ago, the immense forces connected with the collision between the European and the African plates came into direct play. They led to the corrugation and raising of the entire previously accumulated sedimentary sequence. This was the Alpine orogeny that led to the formation, as explained above, of the entire Alpine chain. Later on, the major role in shaping the mountains was played by the various processes of erosion that sculpted and modeled the existing rock to create the landscape we see today. The action of the glaciers, which for a long time extended over much of the Dolomite area, were fundamental in this process.

THE TERRITORY OF THE DOLOMITE ALPS

The Himalayas, the Alps, and the Rocky Mountains are very different mountain chains. And yet, it is not always possible to distinguish among them in photographs. A rocky peak, the green of the trees, a little snow in the shaded gorges: in such images, almost all the mountains of the world look alike.

Almost, but not all. The Dolomite Alps are an exception, and it is enough to have been there for even one short day to recognize them ever after. The Dolomites are unequaled anywhere in the world and it is impossible to confuse this mountain group with any other. It may be the color contrasts, between the pink of the living stone and the dark green of the forests below. Or it may be the play of slopes, the nude spires with their vertical walls reaching almost impudently to the sky, stone soldiers stationed in Alpine summer pastures with their tiny Christmas-card towns.

The simple truth is that the Dolomites are special mountains - unique and unrepeatable - and this is a good point of departure for any tour.

Geographically, the mountainous area known as the Dolomite Alps, or Dolomites, is delimited to the east and in part to the south by the Piave river, and the upper course of the Brenta stretches the boundary toward the west. To the west proper, the area is bounded by the Adige and the Isarco rivers and to the north by the Rienza that runs through the Val Pusteria. The exception are the Brenta Dolomites, which rise on the other side of the Adige river as an isolated group even though they are true Dolomite formations to all effects.

Seeing is believing: the Dolomites are mountains so peculiar that they are immediately recognizable, so different are they from any of the surrounding mountains.

In this particularly vast mountain group, subgroups have been identified, with names of various types: the Dolomites of Cadore, the Dolomites of Sesto, the Dolomites of Ampezzo - or Eastern and Western Dolomites. Another type

A close-up of the crest of the Forcella Staunies in the Cristallo group, against the backdrop of the lovely Dolomiti di Sesto.

of distinction is administrative, since the mountains are parceled out among the Italian provinces of Trento, Bolzano, and Belluno, where some signs of past political tensions still linger. These mountains were the site of many battles over the border between Italy and Austria, and traces of the sadly-famous trenches and fortifications of times past still remain to explain today's geopolitical administrative subdivisions.

If we want to get to know the Dolomite Alps as mountains, however, we must first of all learn to consider them a single group; if, instead, we want to understand the culture of the different populations that inhabit the region, we must simply accept the administrative boundaries and learn to distinguish the different cultures - but neither do these always fit with the borders, as we will see later on.

If we look closely, we will notice that the subdivision of the populations only follows the physical divisions imposed by the forces of nature that for so many centuries have been the supreme authority in this area.

When we enter the Dolomite region, whether it be by train, car, or bus, our first view is always from below and for this reason it is the valleys, more than the mountain groups that surround them, that the tourist knows best.

The culture, the cuisine, and even the language of the peoples that inhabit the valleys, narrow strips of land driven in like wedges among the mountains that from their peaks dominate different regions, change from one side to the other of the same mountain. In this sense, the Dolomite Alps may be considered the ethnic watershed of central Europe. After having crossed a pass, like

The many ethnic groups in the region have maintained their single cultural identities. Below, a young woman in the traditional costume of Cortina d'Ampezzo; right, folk costumes of the Gardena area.

the Pordoi, we often find ourselves among people speaking a different **language** and enjoying a different **cuisine**. Even the **architecture**, which while still of the Alpine genre exhibits striking differences, changes in the space of those few kilometers. But this is not as strange as it may seem. For centuries, these mountains represented insurmountable obstacles for the valley-dwellers for a good part of each year. During the long winter months, but even in summer, before the wide modern roads were built, it was easier to descend a valley to procure needed food, clothing, and tools in the nearby plains areas than to cross the natural barrier of altitude and snow. Thus the culture that developed in the Val di Fassa mirrored that of Trento, while beyond the Marmolada and the Passo del Falzarego, Cortina and the Cadore region depended almost exclusively on the Venetian merchants and developed in parallel but independently, supplying wood for the ships of the Republic of Venice. On the other side, beyond the Sella massif, Ortisei, Santa Cristina, and Selva, the largest towns of the Val Gardena, communicated mainly with Bolzano, while the Val Badia, with Corvara, Colfosco, and the nearby La Villa, San Cassiano, and San Vigilio, always had more to do with Austria than with the Italian territories. In terms of simple distance, the valleys lie close together, but their peoples had so little contact with one another for so long that the differences that evolved are still palpable today.

The division of the area into the Italian provinces of Trento, Bolzano, and Belluno separates the Dolomites into valleys with Trentine, Tyrolese, and Venetian cultural influences. Such sharp distinctions are found at no other Italian regional boundaries.

Facing page, the Ampezzo basin and Monte Pelmo seen from the Forcella Staunies.

HISTORY AND TRADITIONS

The long history of the mountains stretches back to extremely remote times. The abundant fauna attracted the hunters of the Paleolithic era in the summer, and traces of settlements are not a rarity. The oldest archeological sites are on the **Campon di Monte Avena** at 1430 meters above sea level; the finds date to the time of Neanderthal man; that is, about 40,000 years ago, when the climate in the plains was essentially tropical. The later ice ages drove men from the mountains, and the next traces of settlements date to only after the glaciers had retreated, about 12,000 years ago.

It was on the northern slopes of the **Val Fiorentina**, and more precisely in the town of Mondeval de Sora (2150 meters above sea level), that the oldest grave in Europe was discovered. It dates to the Upper Mesolithic (more than 7000 years ago), and the skeleton is that of a hunter, buried with various tomb furnishings; the remains are preserved in the Val Fiorentina museum. Human occupation of these lands became an established fact about 5000 years ago, when with the start of stock-breeding activities the domestic animals were taken to the high pastures in the summer - but man was still a seasonal visitor.

The first permanent settlements arose only much later. The need to defend their possessions, tools, and animals, induced the people to build fortified villages, sturdy citadels strategically positioned on the dominant highlands. The best finds from these times of early settlement are those of the **Alto Adige** area (Vandoies di Sopra, Castelrotto, San Pietro di Fiè), while the **Val Gardena** and the **Val Pusteria** have proven to be true treasure troves of Bronze Age finds. Lagole, in the **Cadore** region, is instead the site of remains of a sort of a 'paleo-venetian' sanctuary, a votive treasury, and ample collections of objects and votive offerings now on exhibit in the local museums.

In 400 BC, the Celts descended on the area and drove the early Venetians off their highlands. The Etruscans exerted pressure from the south, although in their case the coercion took the form of cultural influence rather than armed attack. Thus, even nearly three millennia ago, the Dolomite

these mountains: building ships for the expanding naval power required good wood, and the Dolomite forests were a precious source of raw materials. In 1420, the Magnificent Community of Cadore formally accepted the protection of the Republic of Venice, while the Alto Adige was first under Bavarian rule (during the Napoleonic era) and then became part of the Hapsburg empire until World War I, when it was annexed to Italy.

The Dolomite territory was again a divided land, a border made of mountains between peoples of different languages and customs, and often at war the ones with the others.

1508 saw a particularly merciless encounter between the Republic of Venice and the troops of the Empire, in the Battle of Val Cadore. The Venetians, led by Bartolomeo d'Alviano, repulsed the invaders, who came mainly from the Val Pusteria. But a year later the imperial troops won out

Alps were already a point of demarcation among different cultures.

It was not until Roman times that some sort of uniformity among the different Dolomite areas was achieved. The Via Claudia Augusta, which linked Italy with Bavaria, ran through the Adige valley and notably increased the flow of travelers in both directions. The mountains nevertheless remained an important natural barrier that divided Rome's most vulnerable territories from those occupied by the barbarians to the north, and this fact discouraged development of any more extensive communications routes.

With the fall of Roman Empire, what are today the Venetian Dolomites were occupied by the Lombard clans, who were in turn subdued by the Franks in the 8th century. The Alto Adige was colonized by Germanic peoples from Bavaria, who built permanent settlements and left their distinctive mark on the territory.

The strategic importance of the Alpine passes in no way guaranteed their serenity; rather, the fact brought many lords to these lands, each desiring to guarantee the safety of his borders. In about the year 1000, the Dolomites were part of the Holy Roman Empire, which actually had little or nothing Roman about it. It was the Republic of Venice that again brought Italians to

Above, the entrance to the Museo Etnografico Regole d'Ampezzo in Cortina; right, the remains of ancient populations in an exhibit hall of the Museo Tridentino di Scienze Naturali (Trento).

THE GREAT WAR

A look at the history of World War I can help us to better understand the borders and the tensions that divided these peoples in past centuries (and in some cases, even recently). On the Marmolada, in the Tofane group, or in the area of the Tre Cime of Lavaredo, traces of the old trenches are not an uncommon sight. These areas were the theater of battles among men who today are attempting to live together in peace. World War I resulted in Italy's annexation of territories in which the two major ethnic groups lived together under the Austrian flag: although the flag changed, the people remained the same, united and at the same time divided by language and tradition.

More than by words, in a very real sense the Great War is better explained by the remains, the mementos, and the memories that many of these people have preserved and in which the Dolomites abound.

and the border was established at what is today Dogana Vecchia; Cortina remained under Austrian government.

Later, Venice's union with the new Kingdom of Italy increased tensions along what had become the border between two great nations. The presence of Italian-speaking peoples in Austrian territory was the principal cause of Italy's entry into World War I. The outcome of the war, with the annexation of the entire Dolomite territory to Italy, again unified peoples that over the course of history had been divided

The galleries and vie ferrate used by troops during World War I.

The heritage of the many cultural pockets still existing in the Dolomite valleys is preserved in objects, such as this wooden cart, that in ancient times were commonly used.

marked and require no special athletic preparation, and missing them means missing some of the most beautiful landscapes the area has to offer. Famous groups like the Tre Cime of Lavaredo or the Torri del Vaiolet, for example, do not look their best from the road - and the morphology of the terrain makes it simply impossible to penetrate the interior of the massif by car. There is thus no choice but to go there on foot and find the most panoramic observation point - but always, the effort involved is well rewarded. In short, it is impossible to fully appreciate the Dolomite Alps without walking a little.

The possible summer excursions through the Dolomites run from a walk along a valley bottom to a sixth-level climb. In short, something for everyone.

The excursions described in this guide are for everyone: the so-called 'classics' that are a must in the program of anyone wanting to get to know these mountains. Rock-climbing enthusiasts will find many **specialized publications** as well as the on-site assistance of **expert guides**. The local tourist offices organize climbs up this or that peak for groups of different skill levels. We heartily recommend consulting these experts, since the cliffs in these mountains are often quite difficult and the climber who underestimates them is rarely afforded a second chance.

longer than they had been united.

But the differences are jealously preserved, and each valley has used every available means to consolidate its local history and customs. Many **ethnic museums** have been founded; they contain collections of objects, documents, and historical finds with which each valley preserves its peculiar identity. The material not only aids in rediscovering the old traditions but also provides an easily-assimilable panorama of the development of the single populations.

SUMMER EXCURSIONS

In summer, the Dolomites are literally invaded by tourists of every nationality, but their number falls off abruptly as soon as we stray a bit from the refuges or the arrival points of the lift facilities. This is a shame, because the trails are well-

HIKING EQUIPMENT

CLOTHING:
High shoes that support the ankle, with channeled soles; better if waterproof.
Wool or terry socks, since thin socks may cause blisters.
A spare undershirt in case it gets too hot, and something heavy for emergencies. The weather can change very quickly in the mountains and in these cases a cotton sweatshirt is preferable to a wool sweater, since it 'breathes' better. A waterproof poncho is also a must, since

sudden showers are not uncommon. Comfortable, non-irritating underwear. If your hiking clothes (shorts, tee-shirts, etc.) leave parts of the body uncovered, protect your skin with sunscreen. The sun in the mountains is stronger than on the plains, and can cause serious sunburn.

A map of the area with clear indication of the trails and the refuges, if possible in 1:25,000 scale.

A cell phone is more a fad than a necessity. But in case of accident ...

There now exist portable GPSs that use geostationary satellites to calculate your position, but these devices are useful only if you wander off the trails.

A last thought: you will be car-

EQUIPMENT:

A large, good-quality backpack. Less expensive packs tire your back.

A small first-aid kit with disinfectant, a tourniquet, a snake poison syringe, band-aids (indispensable in case of blisters), and antihistamines for allergy sufferers, since the mountains are the kingdoms of flowers and pollen abounds here. Also an elastic bandage, gauze, a pocket-knife, and lenitive stick in case you are stung by bees, wasps, or other insects. A rope 8 to 10 meters in length can aid in getting across difficult stretches of trail. A small flashlight, with spare batteries, can be a lifesaver if you miscalculate the distance and are caught out at night. Sunglasses are an important accessory.

rying everything for kilometers and kilometers, so be sure it's only the bare necessities.

PROVISIONS:

Water is the most important thing, since lack of liquids causes a rapid imbalance of salts in the body; the typical symptom is cramps in the leg muscles. But neither is it worthwhile to carry liters and liters, because water is heavy.

We suggest exploiting the refreshment stations insofar as possible, and carrying a half-liter canteen of water. Avoid cans and sparkling beverages.

Prepare enough sandwiches for the entire hike; we suggest light, nourishing fillings, neither salty nor spicy. A small store of chocolate and dried fruit is an excellent source of fast energy.

A freeze-frame of a summer excursion on the Alpe di Siusi.

THE VIE FERRATE

*T*he vie ferrate or 'equipped **climbing paths**' are difficult stretches of excursion trails or climbing routes that have been made more accessible by the addition of metal fixtures of various sorts (hence the name, from the Italian ferro = 'iron'). In truth, there are different types of vie ferrate, like the 'partially-equipped paths' in which the fixtures appear only in the most difficult stretches, while the rest is an easy hike, the 'equipped path' proper, which is more difficult, with fixtures everywhere, and the 'equipped climbers' path', where the fixtures are kept to a minimum to preserve the Alpine quality of the route.

It goes without saying that there are many different levels of difficulty and that these trails are in any case not recommended for the casual excursionist, those suffering from vertigo, or those who are not in good overall physical condition. In order for the fixtures (mainly railings or metal ladders) to be of any help, besides normal hiking gear (boots, suitable clothing, etc.) the climber must wear a harness with snaplinks for hooking onto them in the most dangerous points. Since the equipped paths are mostly located on rock walls, the danger of falling rocks should not be underestimated: you will therefore need gloves and above all a sturdy climber's helmet. But the most important piece of equipment is the energy dissipater. Despite the harness, the consequences of a fall of even a few meters would be catastrophic for the body. The energy dissipater is the only tool capable of limiting this kind of damage. Two words of warning. These metal fixtures have often been in place on the mountains for a long time, during all of which they have suffered the attacks of atmospheric agents. Rely on them, surely, but not blindly: always test their strength before attempting a difficult climb or crossing. Furthermore, since metal is a good conductor of electricity, never even consider climbing an equipped path if thunderstorms are forecasted. The metal may act as a lightning rod, and what- and who-ever is attached to it when lightning strikes will be included in the circuit.

In practice, the vie ferrate are an 'easy' way of tackling the mountains for those who do not feel up to actual climbing, but this does not mean that the risks involved are not generally much higher than they seem at first glance.

Remember: if a stretch of the mountain has been equipped with fixtures, it means that it is dangerous, and a metal rope will certainly not suffice to make it easy to climb.

Hikers on a via ferrata on the Catinaccio Rosengarten.
On the facing page, a hiking trail at the foot of the Sella.

WWI AND WWII IN THE DOLOMITE AREA MUSEUMS

MUSEUMS FOR REMEMBERING

**MUSEO STORICO CULTURALE 1915-18 / 1943-45
Campo, Alano di Piave (BL)
Phone 0439 779020**
A scale model, about 7 meters square, shows the territory of the town as it was divided up among the various armed forces in the years 1915-1918. Much material, including shells, grenades, bayonets, rifle barrels, muskets, pistols, rocket guns, daggers, and mauls, is also on exhibit.
Two display cases contain regimental cards, documents, photographs, military maps, and period newspapers.

**MUSEO DELLA GRANDE GUERRA IN MARMOLADA
Accessible only by cableway from Malga Ciapela (BL)
Phone 0437 522984
Open every day**
The museum is located at an altitude of 2950 meters above sea level, at the site of one of the harshest battles between Italians and Austrians, at the edge of the Marmolada glacier. Weapons, uniforms, documents, photographs, and other material is exhibited. A series of guard walks and galleries beginning at the museum lay the trail for an open-air historical walk of over an hour.

**MUSEO DEL MATERIALE BELLICO - 1915 - 1918
Caorera, Vas (BL)
Phone 0439 788014
By reservation only**
The museum, set in the Madonna del Piave park, today counts about two thousand items, including sealed muskets, pistols, helmets, uniforms, bayonets, machine-guns, and other war material from the period as well as documents and maps relating to Caporetto and the Piave front. The museum is housed in two rooms on the ground floor of the parish house.

**MUSEO NAZIONALE STORICO DEGLI ALPINI
Doss Trento (TN)
Phone 0461 233470**
In a former Austrian arsenal donated by the city of Trento to the Acropoli Alpina foundation. In the interior of the museum is a crypt containing the Memorial Chapel with the Gold Medals for Military Valor won by the Italian Alpine Corps from 1896 through 1945. Showcases display personal effects, weapons, photographs, and documents relevant to the history of the famous 'Black Feathers' corps.

ETHNIC MUSEUMS

**'RASSEGNA ATTREZZI E OGGETTI DEL PASSATO'
Via Sperti
Phone 0437 30828
Open only the last Sunday of each month**
A collection of tools and objects no longer in use; more than a thousand items linked to local crafts activities.
More specifically, the museum exhibits tools used by wood-cutters, chair-makers, clogmakers, cartwrights, carpenters, wood-turners, stone-cutters, shoemakers, knife-grinders, wool and hemp carders, etc. There are also many typical kitchen utensils.

**'LA FUDINA' EXHIBIT SPACE
Dosoledo (BL)
Largo IX Febbraio
Phone 0435 67021
By reservation only**
The Regola palace in Dosoledo di Comelico Superiore (Belluno) hosts a reconstruction of an old ironmonger's shop, with products and period tools and machines used for iron-working.

**'LA STUA'
ETHNOGRAPHICAL MUSEUM
Casamazzagno di Comelico Superiore (BL) - Via San Leonardo, 11 - tel. 0437/32397
By reservation only.**
The museum was founded in 1988 with the declared purpose of perpetuating local culture and of collecting documentation illustrating the typical features of the population, lifestyles, traditions, customs, and arts and crafts. It contains a complete reconstruction of a typical old home of Comelico, and in particular of the cellars, the kitchen, the stua or dining room, and the bedroom. Other rooms in the museum exhibit tools for processing wool and hemp and for other agricultural and pastoral activities.

**RA REGOLES MUSEUMS
Cortina (BL)
Corso Italia, 67
Phone 0436 866222
Open July through September and December through March.**
The Ciasa Ra Regoles contains three different museums all with the same schedule: the Museo Paleontologico Rinaldo Zardini, the Museo Etnografico Regole d'Ampezzo, and the Museo d'Arte Moderna Mario Rimoldi.

MUSEO ETNOGRAFICO REGOLE D'AMPEZZO (see Ra Regoles Museums)
The museum of the traditions of Ampezzo exhibits the utensils and tools typical of the agricultural/sylvan/pastoral culture, plus many works by great craftspeople.
The artistic crafts items on display include examples of metalwork (wrought iron, embossed copper, and silver filigree) as well as items in fine woods inlaid with mother-of-pearl and metal wires, period costumes, and teaching collections.

**MUSEO DEGLI USI E COSTUMI DELLA GENTE DI GOIMA
Goima di Zoldo Alto (BL)
Former elementary school
Phone 0437 797085
Open in July-August and December-January
Other periods by reservation only**
Inaugurated in 1987, this museum exhibits materials inherent to the history, economy, dialect, folklore, and customs of the people of the Goima valley, and sponsors teaching activities aimed at perpetuating the ancient traditions.
The exhibits range from agriculture to metallurgy, carpentry, spinning, and the footwear industry, and include a reconstruction of an ancient stua with its typical fornel. Almost all of the material on exhibit is of local production.

**MUSEO DELLA CULTURA ALPINA DEL COMELICO E SAPPADA
Padola (BL)
Largo Calvi
Phone 0437 67149
Open in the summer
Other periods by reservation only**
The museum, sponsored by the local Comunità Montana, contains scale models of the living and working spaces of times past and an exhibit illustrating the use of the horse in local activities. The stua, the kitchen, and the bedroom are reproduced in full-scale reconstructions featuring objects loaned or donated to the museum by the people of the area.
There is also a collection of typical local costumes,

and much other material and photographs.

MUSEO ETNOGRAFICO DEGLI ZATTERI DEL PIAVE
Codissago di Castellavazzo (BL)
Former elementary school
Phone 0437 772373-771057
Open Saturdays and Sundays, by reservation only
The rafts that transported wood along the Piave river were for centuries one of the hinges of the economy of the Belluno area and above all of that of Codissago di Castellavazzo and the Longarone district.
The thousand-or-so items on exhibit in the museum illustrate the evolution of rafting in chronological order from prehistorical to historical times up until the advent of the railroad.

MUSEO DELLA MAGNIFICA COMUNITÀ DI CADORE
Pieve del Cadore (BL)
Piazza Tiziano, 2
Phone 0435 32262
Open in winter, by reservation only
The museum, founded in 1980, exhibits pre-Roman and Roman age fragments from the votive cache of Lagole.
The finds, which amount to about a thousand pieces mainly from the central area, create a clear picture of the local settlements, especially pre-Roman Venetian civilization.

MUSEO DEGLI USI E COSTUMI DELLA GENTE TRENTINA
San Michele all'Adige (TN)
Phone 0461 650314
This museum, in the old Augustinian monastery of San Michele all'Adige, contains more than 40 rooms for a total exhibit area of 2500 square meters, with almost 9000 items all inherent to rural technology in the moun-

tains. A broad-ranging reconstruction of the ethnographic history of the Trento area.

MUSEO PINACOTECA DELLA MAGNIFICA COMUNITÀ DI FIEMME
Cavalese (TN)
Phone 0462 502392
The museum exhibits originals and copies of the most important documents of the Magnificent Community of Fiemme, including the first Statues, or regulations applicable to the valley, along with minor documentary evidence of family life and the tools of olden times. Also on display are many canvases of the school of Fiemme.

MUSEO LADINO DI FASSA
Vigo di Fassa (TN)
(for information:
Istituto di Cultura Ladina
Phone 0462 764267)
An ethnographic exhibit that offers a summary of aspects of traditional society in Fassa and of Ladin culture as expressed in work and community life.

MUSEO DELLA CIVILTÀ SOLANDRA
Malè (TN)
Open summer, Christmas, and Easter
(for guided tours:
Phone 0463 901272)
Collects evidence of everyday life and mountain civilization in the Val Sole: means of subsistence, crafts, and household, agricultural, and cheese-making tools and equipment.

MUSEO DELLA VAL GARDENA CESA DI LADINS
ORTISEI (BZ)
PHONE 0471 797554
A collection of items illustrating Ladin culture. The section containing wooden sculptures, a typical valley craft, is very interesting. A portion of the museum is

dedicated to naturalistic and archaeological exhibits.

MUSEO DELLA COLLEGIATA DI SAN CANDIDO
San Candido (BZ)
Phone 0474 913278
Open from 1 June to 15 October
A collection of archaeological finds (prehistorical and Roman, from the ancient Littamum) from the area. A second section displays old agricultural and crafts tools from Val Pusteria.

MUSEO DEGLI USI E COSTUMI DELLA PROVINCIA DI BOLZANO
Teodone, Brunico - Dietenheim (BZ)
Villa Santa Caterina
Phone 0474 550781
Seasonal opening hours
An interesting open-air section with a series of rural constructions typical of the southern Tyrol region (including a hay-barn with a straw roof). A 16th-century building contains a separate collection of objects pertaining to farming life and local tradition.

VAL DI FIEMME VAL DI FASSA VAL CISMON THE DOLOMITES OF TRENTO

These mountains, with the Val di Fiemme, the entire Val di Fassa, and stretching to San Martino di Castrozza, are those that have had the most to do with the nearby city of Trento. On the other side of the Adige river, the same influence invested the Brenta Dolomites, a mountain group that is physically detached from the others but with very similar characteristics, but in this area the influence of the Po valley culture was stronger.

Over time, the Adige valley in fact emerged as a line of cultural as well as geographical demarcation: the differences in architecture and cuisine in Madonna del Campiglio and Val di Fassa, for example, although slight, are significant.

The language is clearly Italian, with no influences of particular note; Ladin is found more on paper than in practice. The architecture is typically Alpine, with wooden homes with flower boxes at the windows, but with strong Italic overtones. The walls are mostly in masonry work, and wood is used primarily for decoration. Various styles, from rustic cabins and modern residences, alternate with what is sometimes exasperating promiscuity. Overall, the demands posed by modern tourism have canceled out much of the original architecture on both sides of the Adige.

THE VAL DI FIEMME

This is a wide valley on the way to the more famous Val di Fassa, its ideal continuation. Delimited by the Lagorai group on the one side and the Latemar on the other, it is for all practical purposes the gateway to the Dolomites for those arriving from the south.

The Val di Fiemme is the lower course of the **Avisio**, a clear stream that rises at the Passo Fedaia and flows into the Adige near Trento.

While the fastest way to the valley is to exit the superhighway at Ora, about halfway between Trento and Bolzano-Bozen, it is worthwhile choosing the longer route, exiting at Trento and taking the road that leads through the Val di Cembra directly to Cavalese. This valley, slightly outside the Dolomite region as such, is famous for its porphyry quarries. Locally, the stone is called 'red gold'; it is the paving material for many an Italian

Below, the beautiful Norway spruce and Swiss pine woods on the slopes of the Sass Putia at the Passo delle Erbe.

A stretch of the course of the Avisio, the stream that flows through the Val di Fiemme and the Val di Fassa.

street. In Segonzano, stop to see the famous **Piramidi di Segonzano**, or the Omeni as they are called by the inhabitants of the area. This interesting formation was created by erosion, by water, of the soft morainal accumulations. Large blocks of stone have defended the underlying material and have remained isolated from the rest, which has instead taken the form of spires, many exceeding ten meters in height. The spectacle is decidedly suggestive and in continual evolution.

Cavalese is the first sizable town in the Val di Fiemme. It lies in a broad, grassy basin and has a history all its own and an art collection in the Palace of the Magnificent Community of Fiemme. Of medieval origin, the building was abandoned in the 18th century (after having served even as a place of custody pending trial) and was restored in 1935. The facade is adorned with 16th-century frescoes.

It is in Cavalese, during the last week of January, that the more than six thousand participants in the **Marcialonga**, the most important cross-country ski event in the Dolomites (and not only here), conclude their trek of more than 70 kilometers.

Three kilometers from Cavalese, in Castello Molina di Fiemme, at the foot of the Doss Zelor, are some important remains of imperial-age Roman homes.

Predazzo, the second important center in the Val di Fiemme, is situated at the fork between the Val di Fassa and the lesser-known Val Travignoto, which leads to the Passo Rolle and to San Martino di Castrozza. It was at one time an important iron and copper mining town; today, it is known for its woodworking and a particular local white marble called predazzite, from the name of the town.

*Left and below, the pyramids of
earth at Segonzano,
in Val di Cembra.*

FROM CANEDERLI TO STRUDEL

*T*he cuisine is typical of the Mediterranean area and at the same time typically Alpine with many traditional 'poor' dishes of peasant origin, for example the smacafam. The extensive apple orchards for which the Val di Non is famous have influenced the **culinary history** of the region: apples are the primary ingredient in a myriad of dishes, from hors-d'oeuvres to desserts. Canederli, originally imported from the north, is now counted among the typical dishes of the area, although other dishes are much more so: stewed tripe, macaroni pie, Trentine ravioli, eel and trout (both prepared Trento-style), salt cod 'alla Cappuccina', omelets, bean cakes, baldonazzi, fiadoni, grostoli, rosada, taiadele smalzade, dumplings, Luganega sausage with polenta and mushrooms, tonco de pontesel, sguazzett, *rabbit with dark polenta*, 'Simona cake', and the eternal strudel.

In these valleys we also find the classical Alpine cheeses, all produced with pure cows' milk, like Trentine grana and Asiago, Spressa, and many other, basically very similar, local hard varieties, or the soft varieties, all of which melt and all rather fatty.

The charcuterie products are excellent and highly imaginative: combinations of würstel-type bases with additions of flavorings like olives and peppers.

The temptation is strong - and all things considered it's worthwhile succumbing. Among the various specialties, the famous pork hock, which can be found nearly everywhere, is a treat not to be missed.

The many wine cellars are supplied by the many small local distilleries with aromatic grappas in the most fanciful flavorings, usually based on Alpine herbs. The local wines are all relatively light and bear the unmistakable denominations 'Trentino rosso', 'Trentino bianco', and 'Trentino Cabernet'.

By and large, the cuisine in the Trento area is extremely rich and varied, possibly the best in the Dolomite milieu.

Polenta and the apples of the Val di Non are never lacking on the tables in these valleys.

APPLE STRUDEL
of the Val di Non

INGREDIENTS: *300 g (12 oz) prepared puff pastry; 1 Kg (2 lbs) Golden Delicious apples; 100 g (4 oz) dry bread crumbs; 100 g (4 oz) sugar; 40 g (2 oz) pine nuts; 40 g (2 oz) raisins; 1 teaspoon powdered cinnamon; grated rind of 1 lemon; 1 beaten egg yolk.*

Peel, core, and slice the apples. Combine with the sugar, pine nuts, raisins, cinnamon, lemon rind, and bread crumbs, reserving a few tablespoons. Roll out the puff paste dough as thinly as possible; cut two half-inch strips and set aside. Sprinkle the remaining bread crumbs over the rolled-out dough and cover with the filling, leaving the edges of the dough free; brush the edges with a little of the beaten egg yolk.

Form a roll, taking care not to roll too tightly; close the ends. Place on a buttered baking sheet and brush with the rest of the egg yolk. Decorate the surface with the reserved strips of dough in a lattice pattern.

Bake for about 30 minutes at 200°C (400°F). Allow the strudel to stand for a few minutes and serve dusted with confectioner's sugar.

DOLOMITE MINERALS

*E*xploitation of the mineral wealth of the Dolomites goes back far in time. At the beginning of the 13th century there already existed precise regulations governing the extraction of silver from the mines (today worked out) of Mount Celisio near Trento. Certainly since that time, but in all probability even since earlier eras, the area has sparked interest from an industrial points of view - and more simply, among collectors.

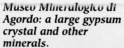

Even the name of this mountain chain recalls its mineralogical importance. The name Dolomites or Dolomite Alps derives from a mineral discovered here in the 18th century called **dolomite** - even though among all the minerals found here dolomite is surely one of the less interesting for the afficionado of beautiful, rare crystals. The mineral wealth of the Dolomites is in fact enormous: something like 350 different mineral species exist in the Dolomites proper and outlying areas, and in the majori-

ty of cases the crystals of the samples found here are exceptional. Most often the minerals can be found in geodes of basaltic rock or in the areas of contact between rocks of sedimentary origin and others of igneous origin. The most beautiful minerals in the region have been found in the Predazzo-Monzoni area.

They were formed 230 million years ago by metamorphism, when masses of magma and sedimentary rock came into contact. This is the case, for example, of fassaite, which takes its name from the Val di Fassa where it is found in the metamorphic calcareous rocks, and of vesuvianite, gehlenite, anorthite, and the garnets. Considering the enormous number of mineral species found in the Dolomites, it is impossible to deal even summarily with such a vast subject in this guide, but mineral lovers will find mineralogy texts in any bookstore in the region.

Museo Mineralogico di Agordo: a large gypsum crystal and other minerals.

THE VAL DI FASSA

The Val di Fassa extends along a deep, hook-shaped glacier trough about twenty kilometers in length. It is one of the most beautiful of the Dolomite region valleys, at least landscape-wise, since it is situated among some of the area's most

majestic mountains in an absolutely spectacular cornice. On the left, the **Latemar** first and then the **Catinaccio** precede one of the best-known groups in the Dolomites, the **Sassolungo**, formed of three independent pinnacles that are perfectly visible from halfway up the valley. Ahead looms the **Sella** group, a gigantic sugar-

All the power of the Latemar group that dominates the Val d'Ega, the Val di Fiemme, and the Val di Fassa.

On the pages that follow, the steep walls of the Catinaccio d'Antermoia seen from Pera di Fassa.

The Sella massif and the Piz Boè, from Monte Fernazza.
Right, the town of Moena at the mouth of the
Val di Fassa.
Facing page, top, the walls of the Catinaccio
d'Antermoia
(on the left) and the Monzoni group, which flank the
middle course of the Val di Fassa; bottom, the Sella
massif seen from Canazei.

loaf of rock that is in a sense the heart of the Dolomites, since it is part of the panorama from almost all of the most important and most-visited valleys.

On the right, behind the Monzoni group, the **Marmolada** rises to an imposing 3342 meters, showing its steepest face.

The Val di Fassa is a tourist valley par excellence, offering more than 40,000 beds in hotels, residences, campsites, and other facilities, as opposed to a resident population of only a little over 8000: in the high season, one resident for every five tourists. It is superfluous to point out that the majority of the valley-dwellers work in the tourist sector both summer and winter.

The mouth of the valley is wide and the first im-

Left, Vigo di Fassa, at the turnoff for the Val d'Ega and, below, Pozza di Fassa.
Bottom, a view of the roofs of Canazei with Campitello in the background.

Above, the extraordinary spectacle from the Belvedere di Canazei, with the ski trails, the three peaks of the Sassolungo, and the hulking structure of the Sella.
Right, a summer panorama of Alba di Canazei.

The Torri del Vaiolet

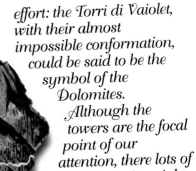

These mountains, wedged between the Catinaccio Rosengarten and the Catinaccio d'Antermoia, 'cost' a bit to see, but the prize at the end of the hike is worth every drop of sweat.

The road that leads to the first refuge is closed to private traffic for a good stretch, so it is worthwhile taking the buses that from the Pozza di Fassa parking lot leave you off about two kilometers below the Rifugio Gardeccia. From here, you must proceed on foot along the Vaiolet Valley that runs between the two Catinacci. The slope, gentle at the beginning, becomes steeper only near the end, when you are already within hailing distance of the Rifugio Preuss set on a rocky spur like a bird in a nest. All around are the soaring pinnacles of the Catinaccio d'Antermoia. The last stretch, which leads up to the Torri as such and the Rifugio Re Alberto, is a fairly difficult climb. The sign says 45 minutes, but it takes good legs to cover the distance in such a short time, considering also that you have to help yourself along with your hands on rock that is often slippery. It is nevertheless worth the effort: the Torri di Vaiolet, with their almost impossible conformation, could be said to be the symbol of the Dolomites.

Although the towers are the focal point of our attention, there lots of other interesting sights. Beyond the towers you can see to the south slope of the Sciliar, which shows us a face that is not often seen and is completely different from the side you see from the Val Gardena. Climbing again, we reach the Passo Santner at 2741 meters above sea level. The panorama is superb: on the left the sheer walls of the Catinaccio Rosengarten, with an equipped path that is anything but easy to climb. Beyond the refuge, instead, the view takes in the long Val di Tires, at the end of which, on a clear day, you can see the city of Bolzano. The view beyond the pass is a true surprise for those who came all the way up here to see the celebrated Torri di Vaiolet. The whole climb takes two to 2½ hours from the bus stop, and a little less to come back down.

The sheer wall of the Catinaccio Rosengarten and, facing, the suggestive Torri del Vaiolet.

*Top, the Torri del Vaiolet and the Rifugio Re Alberto.
Bottom left,, the Rifugio Preuss and right,
an excursion over the Passo Santner,
which overlooks the Val di Tires.*

The panorama from the peak of the Marmolada, looking south.

portant town is **Moena**, whence branches off the road to the Passo di San Pellegrino. The town takes its name from the Lago di Moia, which had formed from the waters of the Avisio in the stretch that today flows through the town.

Moena is a large-scale center that is well organized for summer tourism but less so for winter activities. The medieval **church** of San Volfango, with its frescoes, is worth a visit.

Moena is also the point of departure for a number of sports events. The most important is the famous **Marcialonga**, which involves more than 6,000 athletes the last Sunday in January. The route of this cross-country ski event takes them to Canazei and back and then to Cavalese.

The summer is instead the season for the **Rampilonga**, one of the best-attended mountain-bike races in the world. The course, over 42 kilometers in length, runs from Moena up to the Alpe di Lusia and then descends toward the Parco Naturale di Paneveggio - Pale di San Martino before it returns, through the Passo Lusia, to Moena. The total difference in level, taking only the ascents into account, is about 1900 meters.

The small town of **Vigo di Fassa** is the start of the road that leads to the Passo di Costalunga, and it is also an excellent point of departure for the Catinacci, a group of steep pinnacles accessible only to expert climbers and divided into two distinct groups: the Catinaccio d'Antermoia, which runs in a northerly direction, and the Catinaccio Rosengarten, which flanks the Passo di Costalunga.

The even smaller towns of **Pozza** and **Pera di Fassa** are little more than small resorts. The most active winter tourism begins further up, in Campitello and above all in Canazei.

Canazei is a town blessed by nature with its position among spectacular mountains, and a cableway trip to the **Belvedere** di Canazei is not to be missed in any season. It would be useless to describe the sights, since it would be impossible to succeed in doing justice to the magnificence of nature's show here.

Campitello di Fassa is less important, but the cableway that links the town with Col Rodella offers an excellent vantage point on the same incredible scenario. Both towns are strategic take-off points for summer hikes into the surrounding mountains.

Alba di Canazei closes the valley where it narrows like a funnel. Alba is a small center, so closed-in by the mountains that it is shaded for most of the day; it is nevertheless important because it is the start of the road that leads to the **Lago di Fedaia**, an enormous man-made basin in the heart of the Marmolada that collects the run-off from the glacier. If for no other reason, it is worthwhile going as far as the lake to see the view from its especially panoramic position. From the lake you can take the lift to the Marmolada glacier, famous for its summer skiing. But to reach the peak you must go to **Malga Ciapela**; from here, a three-stage cableway climbs to above the glacier to over 3000 meters, with breathtaking views along the way. The view of the glacier below and out on every side is exhilarating to say the least.

An excursion on the Marmolada glacier. From the top of a crest, the hiker can drink in all the beauty of the Sella massif. Above, the reflection of the massive glacier on the surface of the Lago di Fedaia.

Discovering the Sella

The Sella massif should be considered the focal point of the Dolomites, since so many towns and cultures turn around it. It is the crossroads of four of the most important valleys: the Val Badia, the Val di Livinallongo, the Val di Fassa, and the Val Gardena, which all terminate up against its slopes. The towns of Canazei, Selva di Val Gardena, Corvara, Colfosco, and Arabba all grew up in its shadow, and four passes are required to get around it: Pordoi, Campolongo, Gardena, and Sella. More than a mountain, it is a new world there for the exploring.

Reaching the peak of the Sella group, the Boè, at 3151 meters above sea level, is easier than it seems, and although the last stretch is a bit tiring, the climb is accessible to anyone. There are lift facilities such as the cableway that runs from the Passo Pordoi to the Sas Pordoi, at 2950 meters altitude - only 200 meters below the peak. Whatever way you plan to get there, this is a climb not to be missed. From the peak, the sky over the nearby mountains and the winding road of the Passo Pordoi is enormous; the automobiles below are barely-visible specks. Many of the most famous peaks are easy to recognize, and the view over the Sassolungo and the Marmolada glacier is exceptional. A clear day, a map of the Dolomites, and a pair of binoculars are all you need for an unforgettable experience.

But besides the panorama, the Sella itself at this altitude is remarkable: a sort of stony desert on which nothing but some lichen and here and there cushions of flowers pressed to the earth manage to survive. The gravelly highland slopes down into gigantic gorges, reminiscent of Dante's Inferno.

From the Rifugio Maria, at the arrival point of the cableway, an easy trail leads to the Boè peak; it is a two-hour walk with no great dangers or difficulties. The alternative is to come up from the other side, taking the lift from Corvara or the Passo di Campolongo. Both take you

The flat summit of the Sella is clearly visible from the Marmolada glacier.

to Crep de Munt, in winter the starting point of the Boè ski trail. From here another lift (not always in operation) takes you to the spectacular amphitheater of the Vallon, a natural arch of stone over deep, vertical-walled gorges, from the center of which there leaps a waterfall that in summer is no more than a trickle and in winter a picturesque sheet of ice.

The second of these lifts runs over a circular lake of glacial origin, the Lech de Boè, around which the rare edelweiss flowers. It is to be hoped that the usual warnings about not picking the flowers are superfluous, but remember - besides causing irreparable damage to a unique habitat, this bad habit is severely punished by law.

Whether you arrive on foot or on the chair lift, the Vallon alone, with its spectacular screes (the debris of landslides) where the steinbock is not a rare sight, is well worth a stopover at the Rifugio Kostner.

From the Rifugio Kostner (2500 meters altitude), trail no. 638 takes you to the Piz Boè. It includes a couple of mountain-goat climbs, but is much more spectacular than its alternative, the Sas Pordoi.

The Piz Boè is, all things considered, somewhat of a delusion. It is a peak like any other, only a bit higher, with a tiny refuge and many black birds circling overhead. These are the Alpine choughs, typical high-altitude Corvidae that become the winged lieges of the mountains above certain altitudes. They are generally cheeky and allow you to approach them; some enterprising individuals even accept food from tourists' hands.

But if you really want to get to know the Sella massif you will have to be willing to face the risks involved in one of the most exciting hikes you can imagine: crossing it. To begin with, you will need two vehicles, one of which must be left at the point of arrival: the Passo Gardena or Corvara, according to the route you plan to take. Make use of the lift facilities to save time, since this hike, which we recommend only to people in good physical condition, takes an entire day. To avoid being caught out at night, we suggest leaving early.

Head into the massif from the Sas Pordoi, ignoring the peak and instead choosing trail no. 627, or, more simply, following the signs to the Rifugio Boè. This refuge is practically at the heart of the group and can be reached only on foot; like the Rifugio F. Cavazza del Pisciadù further on, it is open only in the high summer tourist season, generally in July and August. Should you want to cross the Sella in any other period, like June or September, it is worthwhile asking for information before leaving and when in doubt carrying enough water and provisions for the entire excursion.

Amid the rocks of the Sella: a desert highland cut through by deep gorges.

Preceding pages and right, views of the mighty Sella, a truncated sugarloaf of rock with almost vertical walls.
Above, a suggestive wintertime view of the Vallon in the Venetian Dolomites, with Monte Pelmo (left) and the Civetta (right) in the background.

The hiker who reaches the **Rifugio Boè**, in the heart of the Sella massif, will be rewarded with a breathtaking view of that which is probably the most spectacular gorge in the Dolomites: the Val de Mesdì. This valley, if we

The Rifugio Boè, a point of rest and reference in the desertic heart of the Sella.
On the following pages, the Val di Mesdì that cuts the Sella in two; in the background, the Val Badia.

beautiful position above the Lago di Pisciadù in the shadow of the peak of the same name, involves a couple of difficult bits of trail, but everything considered it is no great effort to reach the Passo Gardena through the Val Setus by mid-afternoon.

The **Val de Mesdì** trail is a bit more dangerous, mainly on account of the first portion among the rocks, where some snow remains even in high summer. The slope is slippery and calls for careful stepping, but what awaits us in the valley is well worth the difficulty of that first stretch. The Val de Mesdì, seen from below, is one of the most spectacular landscapes an excursionist can hope to see, with its walls on both sides that rise so high as to block out the sunlight. Arrival at Corvara in the evening.

LOCKING HORNS

*O*ne of the rarer animals in this area is the **steinbock**: reintroduced between the Sorapis and the Marmolada in the 1970s, this exceptional climber has slowly spread to the great parks in the Cortina area, where it has proved to be much more sociable than the roe deer. Differently from the steinbocks of the Gran Paradiso, which allow visitors to approach to 7-8 meters, the Dolomite animals become nervous even at 50 meters and run away if approached more closely. The many visitors to the area are probably a source of anxiety for these animals, which have developed greater diffidence instead of accepting the human intruders. The best observation points are the crests of the Sorapis group and the Parco Naturale Fanes-Sennes-Braies, and the screes of the Sella and the Tre Cime

di Lavaredo, in the Parco delle Dolomiti di Sesto. Courting-season duels among males are quite common; although they would seem to be more violent that those of the roe deer, in truth they are mostly ritualistic and serve to establish hierarchies. The adversaries rear on their hind legs and then drop, careening toward each other until their horns engage: the resounding crash can be heard even from far away. When one of the two decides to break off hostilities, the other does not follow him - and aggressions cease then and there.

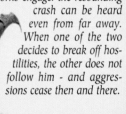

may be so bold as to call it that, is a deep fracture that runs right into the center of the Sella, cutting it in two. The mountains, almost 3 kilometers high, rise sheer both sides and are interrupted only where the equally immense screes slope more gently into a torrent. In some places the floor of the fracture lies almost a thousand meters lower than the peaks - if you suffer from vertigo we do NOT recommend looking down.

At the Rifugio Boè we are thus presented with a choice (which must nevertheless be made beforehand in order to leave the second vehicle): to the left, the Vallone del Pisciadù awaits us, or we may venture into the Val de Mesdì. In the first case, reaching the **Rifugio F. Cavazza**, in a

THE VAL CISMON

Although not generally well-known by name, this is the valley that leads from Fiera di Primiero to the well-known resort of San Martino di Castrozza, set like a gem between the **Pale di San Martino** and the **Lagorai** chain.

Fiera di Primiero was, in the second half of the Quattrocento, an important mining center for the silver of Mount Bedolé, the copper of the Val Vanoi, and the iron of Transacqua. Even though today the town lives mostly on the tourist trade, its remaining typical architecture and its narrow streets with an antique air witness its long history. The lovely 15th-century Gothic parochial **church** has two wooden altars dating to the 11th and 12th centuries.

San Martino di Castrozza, in the shadow of the Pale di San Martino, is the major town: it is modern and characteristic all at the same time and is an excellent starting point for summer hikes on the Pale. First take the chair-lift and then the cableway to the peak of the Rosetta, which offers a beautiful view over the town and, on the other side, an incredible panorama of the central Dolomites: the Tofane group, the Cristallo, the Civetta, and other famous peaks that are all visible although not easily recognizable from this unusual angle of view.

A delightful sunset over the Pale di San Martino on a full-moon evening.
In the inset, San Martino di Castrozza from the Rosetta heights.

THE 'BOSCO DEI VIOLINI'

*D*espite its location in the province of Trento, the influence of Venice was very strong in this valley. The Passo Rolle was at one time a valid natural bulwark; its inhabitants thus depended less on Trento and more on the nearby Feltre, and only naturally adopted its customs, culture, and dialect.

The surrounding **forests** provided the Venetians with timber for building ships that sailed all the world's seas.

The great Italian master Stradivarius came here in the 1700s to select precious woods for crafting his violins and a grove in the Paneveggio forest is still called the Bosco dei Violini in his honor.

The valuable woods of the Val Cismon.

*The panorama from the Passo Rolle at sunset;
far away on the right, the Latemar and, on the left,
the Pala di Santa.*

The Visitors' Center of the Parco Naturale di
Paneveggio - Pale di San Martino organizes guided excursions.

A little above the town, on the side opposite the
Pale, is the Cavallazza plateau with the Colbri-
con lakes. On their shores have been found the
remains of hunters of the Mesolithic era, dating
to 8000 - 9000 years ago.

Beyond San Martino is the **Passo Rolle**, at the
top of a steep road that winds up the slopes of
the Pale. The rocks here exhibit many geological
stratifications, some of which are spectacular
enough to arouse admiration even in non-
geologists. The view from the pass is splendid,
while on the other side it sweeps across the
dense Paneveggio forest to the outlines of the
Pala di Santa and the Latemar in the distance.

An integral part of the natural park is the Paneveggio forest, a few kilometers beyond the Passo
Rolle. It is the largest forest in the Italian Alps,
mostly of Norway spruce, and features learning
trails and an extremely interesting Visitors' Center.

PARCO NATURALE PANEVEGGIO - PALE DI SAN MARTINO

This park, administered by the Provincia Autonoma di Trento and situated in the extreme eastern
portion of the Regione Trentino-Alto Adige, includes the Dolomite group called the **Pale di
San Martino** and a small portion of the **Lagorai
chain**. It is almost cut in two by the San Martino
di Castrozza ski and tourist district, but the two
parts are united to the north by the important
Paneveggio forest. Other forests administered by
the park authorities are those of San Martino di
Castrozza, Valoorda, and Valoanca.

The difficulty of accessing the Pale di San Martino has protected the area from the environmental
point of view. Man's intervention, although intense, has been mainly confined to the valleys
and the San Martino and Passo Rolle ski trails.

The wildlife in this as in other parks has a long
and complex history. The area was once populated by such species as the bear, the wolf, the deer,
the chamois, the Alpine marmot, the wood
grouse, the vulture, and the sparrow hawk. The
deer and the wolf disappeared in the early 1800s;
and following their elimination as competitors for
food and predators, respectively, the roe deer ap-
peared at mid-century. The last brown bear here
was felled in the early 1900s, and not much later

The Paneveggio forest seen from the Passo Valles and the Lagorai chain.
Below, a marmot basking in the sun.

the vultures and the hawks were annihilated. The **chamois** linger on, hidden in the higher mountains, while the **roe deer** are spreading through the woodlands of the valley bottoms and the slopes. The **marmots** have also survived, since they have few enemies; the **deer** reintroduced in the 1960s immediately found their niche and are spreading rapidly in these mountains where they had lived undisturbed for so long before disappearing by the hand of man.

Today there are thus a goodly number of deer and chamois, a flourishing Alpine marmot population, and a true invasion of roe deer, which for some time now have been the

THE LORD OF THE FOREST

*T*he number of **deer** in this area is now on the increase, thanks to efficient species protection measures. Since the deer is a large animal, it requires ample space in which to live and move and for this reason the species populates only broad woodlands such as the Paneveg-gio forest in the park of the same name. Although it is certainly more infrequent to sight a deer than a roe deer, it is nevertheless possible with good binoculars from a high location permitting a good view over the woods of the valley below.

dominant mammals in the park. **Lynxes** have been reported, but it is difficult to be absolutely sure of their presence.

The most interesting situations from the botanical viewpoint are those of the major state-owned forests, which include well-established wooded areas with tall trees and the best and most varied underwood in all of the Dolomites.

The Paneveggio forest is at the heart of the park. Almost 2700 hectares of **fir-woods** fan out in the upper Travignolo basin, bounded by the Lagorai chain, the Pale di San Martino, and the Cime di Bocche, with centuries-old trees as tall as 40 meters.

The Visitors' Center is worth a visit; the layout of the exhibits is excellent and succeeds in expressing complex concepts in a language accessible to everyone. The Center organizes interesting learning hikes through the woods and to the spectacular **Forra del Travignolo**, which can be seen from a shaky suspended bridge. At one time the forest belonged to the Tyrol counts, and became Italian state land only following World War I. Later, when the Regione Autonoma was consti-

The Forra del Travignolo in the Parco Naturale di Paneveggio.

tuted, the Trentino-Alto Adige regional government took over management, which has now passed to the Provincia di Trento. This fortunate series of political/administrative passages, united with the inhabitants' ingrained sense of respect for this splendid Norway spruce forest, have allowed it to come down to us practically intact.

THE BRENTA DOLOMITES

Although this group stands apart from the rest, it is practically identical to the other Dolomites across the Adige. The appearance of the rose-colored rock, the almost vertical spires, the solitary towers, and the walls striped with the char-

RED AND SILVER

*T*he Dolomite **woodlands** are characterized by the Norway spruce (Picea abies) and the silver fir (Abies alba). Although the silver fir is a tree eminently suited to the Dolomite altitudes, it forms woods in only a few areas - at the mouths of the valleys that from Bolzano and Trento snake into the mountains, in some ravines of the Val Gardena, and in some valleys of the Venetian Dolomites, above all near Belluno - and never over great extensions.
The Norway spruce has vaguely rust-colored bark; the distinguishing feature of

the silver fir is represented by the two small white striations on the undersurface of the leaves; those of the Norway spruce are identical on both surfaces. Another evident difference is in the strobila (cones), which are pendent in the Norway spruce and erect and upward-pointing in the silver fir.
The Norway spruce is a pioneering species par excellence; it is capable of colonizing difficult habitats thanks to its root system, which with respect to that of a tree that may exceed 50 meters in height is extremely superficial. The roots never penetrate to more than 50 centimeters depth and this permits the tree to root on a shallow substrate, should nothing better be available: often its bed is a thin layer of soil deposited by the wind on an arid and inhospitable rock wall or scree.
This superficial root apparatus has its advantages - but also its disadvantages. On the one hand it permits the tree to colonize extreme environments that are impossible

for other species; on the other it exposes the plant to the risk of being uprooted by the wind or by snow weighing on its branches. In the woods of the Dolomite region, enormous individuals brought to the ground by tons of snow is not a rare sight.
The tree is resistant to the cold, and grows at altitudes of up to 2000 meters - and higher, in areas with full exposure to sunlight. The pendulous branches give this conifer its typical 'drooping' air; this habit is highly adaptive, however, since it permits the Norway spruce, with its precarious root sys-

tem, to unload snow from its branches quickly and so avoid excessive accumulation.
Thanks to its adaptability, the Norway spruce is the most important forestry tree in all of Europe.

Left, a Norway spruce at the foot of the Sella and, below, the unmistakable pendulous cone of this tree (left) and the double white striation on the lower side of the leaf that is a distinguishing feature of the silver fir (right).

acteristic horizontal ledges is unmistakable. It almost seems as if the Brenta Dolomites are the stray lamb of the flock, identical to all the others but cut off, alone in the midst of different mountains.

For this reason, the valleys that surround the group have an unusual look that is very unlike the 'classical' aspect described thus far.

On the east side there opens the wide **Adige valley**, with the beautiful Lago di Molveno and the Paganella plateau; these are important tourist centers which, despite their lying at the foot of a Dolomite group, in truth have little to do with it. In any case, the spires of the Brenta group that reflect in the waters of the lake are a post-card picture.

The best way to become acquainted with the

The Brenta Dolomites. Although this group is detached from the others, its mountains nonetheless exhibit the same, unmistakable, structure of the other Dolomite formations.
Below, the eastern slope and, bottom, the Pietra Grande group.

Buildings in masonry and timber on the wooded slopes of the Val di Sole.

Brenta Dolomites is to take the western road, whether you enter the mountains through the **Val Rendena** from the Giudicarie or from the north up the Noce river through the broad **Val di Sole**. Even thus the valley presents an ambiguous face: on the one side the Brenta Dolomites, unmistakable with their almost vertical spires similar to a Gothic cathedral: on the other the completely different, darker, and more uniform slopes of the Adamello and the Presanella.

The people of these valleys (Val Rendena to the south, Val di Campiglio at the center, and Val Meledrio to the north) have not been influenced by either Austrian or Venetian culture. They are pure Trentine - with a hint of a Po Valley inflec-

ONCE UPON A TIME

*T*he Val di Sole and the Val di Non (the latter famous for its apple orchards) preserve many examples of ancient architecture, and among these mostly castles. Unfortunately, quite a number are private property and therefore impossible to visit. The most prestigious on the eastern slopes of the Brenta group is the **Thun Castle**, a mass of powerful fortifications above the town of Vigo di Ton. The rise just above Nanno is crowned by what

is probably the most 'Italic' castle in the Trento area: the **Castle of Nanno**, which tradition attributes to the hand of Andrea Palladio. Between Campodenno and Sporminore stands the massive medieval complex of the **Belasi Castle**, and near Spormaggiore the remains of the **Belfort Castle**. The **Bragher Castle** is in a suggestive position surrounded by ravines on the old road from Taio up to Coredo. The two towers of the **Castle of**

Cles, of the barons of the same name, lift above the Lago di Santa Giustina; the **Malgolo Castle** in Malgolo di Romeno is an elegant fortified residence on the other side of the lake. From a green hill above the southern shores, near Tassullo, the **Valer Castle** of the Spaur counts dominates the lake.

A little way up the Val di Sole from its mouth at Mostizzolo is the **Caldes Castle** in the town of the same name. Legend recounts the sad story of the princess Olinda, who locked herself away in the tower because she was denied her love for Arunte, the minstrel. Other medieval tales that keep the ancient atmosphere alive revolve around this and other ruins scattered through the valley, like the nearby **Samoclevo Castle** and the ruins of the Castles of **Ossana** and **San Michele**, the latter with its monumental tower.

tion.

The most important town is **Madonna di Campiglio**, a well-known resort for both summer and winter activities. Its history is practically non-existent, since it is for all practical purposes a recently-built collection of accommodation facilities. In 1872, a man by the name of Giovanni Battista Righi purchased the land on which the town now stands, and with incredible foresight built the first hotel - and the road that leads to Pinzolo, seeing as there wasn't any. Understandably, Righi's statue stands in the main square of the town.

Madonna di Campiglio is first and foremost a ski resort, but it is also the ideal point of departure for summer excursions, since it abounds in lift facilities.

The older **Pinzolo** is essentially a summer vacation spot, in a nonpareil location at the mouth of the spectacular Val di Genova that runs between the Adamello and the Presanella. Traditionally, it was the town of the knife-grinders who plied their trade in the nearby valleys and even further afield. As we enter the town we note the 'Moleta Rendenese', a bronze monument recalling this ancient craft.

A short walk away from the center takes us to the San Vigilio cemetery church, decorated with grandiose frescoes and bas-reliefs. One of the frescoes, entitled *Dance of Death* and dated 1539, is more than 20 meters in length.

More than once destroyed by fires and floods, Pinzolo has nothing left of its typical Alpine architecture and is today a modern town.

A view of Madonna di Campiglio from above: the town is composed almost entirely of hotels and guest facilities.

Excursion

In Val di Genova

Before continuing on to Madonna di Campiglio, we suggest taking a side-trip in Val di Genova. This valley leads away from the Brenta Dolomites between the mountain groups of the Adamello and the Presanella, but it is impossible to ignore it as you move out from Pinzolo and from the Val Rendena. The Val di Genova is home to the wildest country remaining in the area. The impressive Nardis falls, in the lower part of the valley, cascades down for over100 meters. The waterfall is the last point accessible by car; to continue, you must go on foot or take the tourist buses. The spectacle offered by the woods, ravines, and waterfalls is truly unforgettable.

Several easy but interesting hiking trails start out from Madonna di Campiglio. The excursion to the Lago di Nambino starts in town and continues for three kilometers along the road; then, a 20-minute climb takes you to the lake, at 1768 meters above sea level. It is an undemanding walk that would nonetheless be worth many times the effort, since it is amply repaid by the sight of the entire Brenta Group reflected in the small but picturesque mountain lake at the point of arrival. From the other side of Madonna di Campiglio we may take the cabin-lift to the Spinale, in winter the point of departure of numerous ski trails. Even though it is close to the town, the panorama of the Dolomite spires is majestic.

The most sports-minded may want to try to cross the group, but plan ahead since a second car must be left at the Lago di Tovel parking lot.

A little above Madonna di Campiglio is the Campo Carlo Magno, which owes its name to a legend that recounts how in 787 the emperor Charlemagne led his troops through this pass into battle with the Lombards. From the pass, the lifts take you to the Grosté, at 2442 meters. Trail no. 331 descends precipitously to the point at which trail no. 314 leads off to the left. This trail winds through the spectacular Valle di Santa Maria Flavona to the Lago di Tovel. The hike takes about half a day and is all downhill: about 1300 meters difference in altitude from the Grosté to the lake.

The Nardis waterfall at the mouth of the Val di Genova.

THE RED LAKE

*T*he **Lago di Tovel** is a true pearl of the Brenta Dolomites. It can be reached from the north by taking the side road at Tuenno and up a steep stretch to the ample parking facilities at the lake, at 1178 meters above sea level. The lake, which was formed following an ancient landslide that blocked the runoff of the water, is famous for its unicellular alga Glenodinium sanguineum, which at high densities colors the waters of the lake red. Unfortunately, the phenomenon has not occurred for many years, in parte due to human meddling. Attentive conservation measures may make it possible to restore the original conditions, since the alga has not disappeared entirely: it just doesn't achieve sufficient densities to produce the red-color phenomenon. Red water or not, the landscape around the lake, in the whose crystal-clear waters (visibility to more than 10 meters depth in summer) the Dolomite massif is sharply reflected, is well worth the visit.

The beautiful meadows of the Spinale, where the bright thistles flower and, above, the harsh spires of the Brenta Dolomites reflected in the crystalline waters of the Lago di Tovel.

73

Malé is situated in the Val di Sole that delimits the Brenta Dolomites to the north. It is nearer Bolzano, and the first changes in the architecture begin to become noticeable, evidence that the road from Pinzolo is relatively recent. The 11th-century Church of the Assumption in the main square still has one original portal.

If you approach from the south, near Ragoli you may decide to take the turnoff for the tiny hamlet

Right, a rock partridge. With luck, these birds can be spotted at the edges of the woods on the Brenta Dolomite slopes.
Below, the Lago di Nambino at 1768 meters above sea level.

of **Irone**, which was once abandoned but has now been partially reconstructed. The original structure of the small mountain hamlet has nevertheless remained intact, with its typical architecture and winter quarters for the grazing animals.

PARCO NATURALE ADAMELLO-BRENTA

The Brenta Dolomites group is only the eastern wing of the Parco Naturale Adamello-Brenta, which in toto covers almost 62,000 hectares and embraces the entire Brenta group and a large portion of the Adamello and Presanella massifs.

Two completely different environments, with only a geographical link in common.

The fauna of the area is on the whole identical to that of the other Dolomite areas, but the fauna is set apart by the presence of the Alpine **brown bear** - although unfortunately there are only a few individuals left, and it is useless to try to see them. It is much easier to spot **chamois**, **roe deer**, and **deer**. Common birds are the **rock**

MORNING'S MINION

*T*he **roe deer** is increasingly common in the Dolomites, where its natural predators and many of its competitors for food are now scarce., and the situation in some valleys is of overpopulation. Small groups of roe deer grazing at dawn in the clearings is a common sight, but almost exclusively in the valley bottoms or on the slopes exposed to the sun, since the animal does not welcome excessive cold. An early-morning walk along a forest path offers good probabilities of spotting roe deer.

ptarmigan, the **black grouse**, and the **rock partridge**. We will see the **nutcracker** flying in the **Swiss pine** woods, but the **wood grouse**, one of the more valuable species, is harder to spot, is usually well hidden in the underbrush.

One of the few brown bears left in the Parco Adamello-Brenta and, below, a female chamois with her offspring.

THE DOLOMITES OF BOLZANO OR OF ALTO ADIGE

Sixty-five percent of the population of the Alto Adige region are native German-speakers, 5% are native Ladin speakers, and only the remaining 30% speak Italian as their native language. Over time, these differences have created situations of tension and discontent; this was the case in the early 1900s in Trento, an Italian-language city that at the time was under Austrian dominion.

The special statute of autonomy passed in 1972, guaranteeing equal dignity to the different language groups, has in part smoothed over the contrasts, which nevertheless still exist among the most fervent supporters of the different factions.

Luckily these are only isolated episodes: on the whole they are disappearing and may involve the tourist only in localities off the beaten track. The tourist operators, whose livelihood depends on both ethnic groups, have long since learned not to discriminate.

Localities like Ortisei (the largest tourist center of the Val Gardena) and Selva di Val Gardena are true linguistic Babels where three ethnic groups

meet and mix: **Italians**, **Germans**, and **Ladins**. There is therefore nothing odd at all about finding signs in three languages. The localities are tourist-oriented par excellence and hospitality abounds, whatever language the host speaks. These people are usually proud of their linguistic abilities and the good-neighbor relationships they have succeeded in establishing.

Of a decidedly more Austrian cultural leaning is the valley that from Brunico (Val Pusteria) cuts into the Dolomites. It has only a few forks: the first leads to San Vigilio, while the other follows the Val Badia as far as the Sella massif, with Cor-

The enchanting view from the Forcella dell'Ega: the crest on the left separates the Puez from the Odle group.
On the facing page, two examples of the how the three languages of the area coexist.

vara and Colfosco and, on the other side, La Villa, which is in turn the turnoff for San Cassiano and the Passo del Falzarego, another natural barrier.

It is said that the language of these valleys is Ladin, but German is actually the major tongue. The reason is clear: for centuries, the valley dwellers were under Austrian rule and only at the end of World War I (to be more exact, on 10 September 1919), did they realize they had become Italians. The oldest inhabitants of the area still remember another flag and another language, and as is easy to imagine, things haven't changed much in such a short timespan, nor are they likely to in the near future. The culture itself is typically Tyrolean. All the inhabitants speak perfect Italian, but at home they speak German. Their Italian is heavily accented and spoken slowly, in the manner typical of those unused to speaking a language.

Architecture in the Dolomites of the Alto Adige reflects the Tyrolese influence: the roofs are often of dark stone, and the church steeples, like in the Austrian Alps, are more often rounded-off than pointed. The stone homes are often massive and severe-looking, but many buildings are still built of wood: with their windowsills half-hidden by geraniums, they have a pleasant and almost dollhouse look about them.

THE LADIN LANGUAGE

*T*he **Ladin language**, for centuries the major tongue in these mountains, is today in third place after Italian and German. It is still strongly radicated in certain areas, and is officially spoken by 30,000 inhabitants of the four valleys that descend from the Sella: the Val Badia, the Val Gardena, the Val di Fassa, and the Valle di Livinallongo. In the Val di Fassa, Ladin has by now been almost completely superseded by Italian, as it has been by German in the Val Badia, but national and local authorities tend to defend the Ladin culture, which seems to be enjoying a revival even among the younger generations.

Many museums, like the Cèsa di Ladinis in Orsisei, bear witness to the existence of the Ladin culture in these valleys.

Ladin culture and language lives on mostly in the smaller centers. At La Villa in Val Badia, for example, the population is trilingual but with a strong German ascendancy, while in the smaller nearby towns of Larzonei, Crazzolare, Cianins, and Adang, Ladin is used by many as a sort of local dialect - but Castalta and Rislande are totally Ladin localities.

Arabba and the Livinallongo valley, the most isolated among those mentioned above, are located in the very heart of the Dolomites. Although they depend on the Regione Veneto, the inhabitants have kept Ladin culture alive through their own efforts. This is nevertheless a small cultural pocket and the number of permanent residents in this valley is very small. For this reason, the Ladin language and culture are today evident mainly in the Dolomites of Bolzano, in Val Badia, and in Val Gardena.

Right, examples of the architecture of the area, which reflects the German influence (above) in its austerity and grandeur but also the Tyrolese school (right), for instance in the 'onion-top' bell towers.

The most characteristic element of architecture in Alto Adige is the **maso** (in German, the *Hof*), where the rural family once lived. These constructions are built of wood, sometimes over a ground floor in masonry. The house itself is generally flanked by the barn; the oldest barns have thatched roofs. The curious legal obligation, introduced by Maria Theresa of Austria in 1770 and called the *maso chiuso*, assigns the ownership of the *maso* to the firstborn in order to avoid that the property be broken up among many heirs.

The Dolomites of Bolzano have not suffered from much abusive construction, and from afar even the grand hotels seem to be Alpine huts - just a little bigger. Overall, the architecture is the most agreeable in all of the Dolomites, and even recently-built homes reflect the ancient traditions.

Flowered balconies in Val Pusteria. This custom is more common in the Dolomites of Bolzano than in the Venetian or Tridentine Dolomites.

BEYOND WÜRSTEL

*The cuisine is quite different from that of the Trentine and Venetian Dolomites. Würstel, charcuterie, and cheeses: in these areas everything is smoked and the flavors are strong and heady. Perhaps the most typical dish of **Alto Adige** and **Tyrolese cuisine** is würstel, but the smoked meats with kraut, smoked speck, and the great variety of cheeses, butter, and creamed dishes are also famous. There are also the omelets and the barley, knödel (or canederli), and goulash soups, game dishes served with mountain berry sauce, pork specialties like kaminwurzen, platters like herrengröstel (pan-fried meat and potatoes), and many sweets of clearly Austrian origin, like krapfen and strudel (the classical apple but also flavored with poppy seeds or walnuts.)*

In Val Gardena, we find many polenta dishes, typical of the mountains; near Bressanone you may try the piatto dell'elefante, prepared using different meats and owing its name to the 'jumbo' portions.

The wine shops are many in number; although each of the valleys at one time probably has its own tradition, by now, wherever you go, all offer the same local products: Alpine herb liqueurs, liquors based on herbs or juniper-root, Alpine flowers, or gentian, and aromatic grappas.

The jams and jellies are excellent, but production of true mountain honey is quite limited. The hotels offer international fare that changes little from valley to valley, but at the grocers' shops and the butchers' and pork butchers' you will notice evident differences in the cuts of meat and way products are processed. The cuisine here is much more central-European than Mediterranean, and quite varied: while Canazei and Corvara are only a few kilometers apart as the crow flies, the distance between their respective gastronomic traditions is infinitely greater.

CANEDERLI SOUP

INGREDIENTS FOR 14/16 CANEDERLI: 500g (16 OZ - 1 LB) DAY-OLD BREAD; 200 g (8 OZ) HUNGARIAN SALAMI; 200 g (8 OZ) FRESH LUGANIGA (OR OTHER WELL-FLAVORED SAUSAGE); 4 EGGS; 1/2 LITER (1 PINT) MILK; 100 g (4 OZ) FLOUR; FRESH CHIVES; GRATED NUTMEG; BEEF BROTH.

Crumble the bread, add the milk, and allow to stand for about 45 minutes; add the beaten eggs and the sifted flour. Coarsely chop the two meats and stir into the mixture; add the minced chives, nutmeg to taste, and a pinch of salt.
Mix thoroughly and allow to stand for about 10 minutes.
Form into balls (about 5 cm - 2 in) and simmer in a generous quantity of broth for about 15 minutes. Serve very hot.

THE VAL GARDENA

This very well-known valley owes its fame (and its fortune) to its many hotels, excursion trails, and ski trails. The valley runs from the Alpe di Siusi to the Sassolungo to the south and the Odle group to the north, and ends against the Sella massif.

Castelrotto is a bit outside the valley, on the western slopes of the Alpe di Siusi, but is well worth a visit all the same. Although it is a small town, its history is long, as can be seen in the frescoed facades of the houses, the ancient castle, and even the remains of Roman fortifications. Around the 18th-century bell tower that rises above the colorful main square, the small historical center is the best preserved and one of the most distinctive in the entire area of the Dolomites of Bolzano.

Ortisei, the most important center of the Val Gardena, owes its fame to the ski trails of the Alpe di Siusi, which have transformed it into a hotel town. The late-Baroque parish church of Saint Ulrich is noteworthy. Ortisei is the capital of the Gardena woodworking crafts industry, with its art and wood-carving schools and museum, and many small shops that sell nothing but examples of the woodworker's craft.

Santa Cristina is above all a ski resort, famous as the site of many downhill world-championship meets. The trail ends right at the massive towers of Castel Gardena, the medieval abode of the Wolkenstein family.

*One of the characteristic homes of Castelrotto with its frescoed facade.
Facing page: upper left, a view of Ortisei, with its many accommodations for tourists; right and bottom, winter and summer panoramas of the Val Gardena, which owes its fortune to the mountains that surround it and the hospitality it offers tourists and vacationers.*

PARCO NATURALE PUEZ-ODLE-GARDENACCIA

This park, founded only in 1978, embraces the **Odle** mountains and the **Gardenaccia** plateau in the **Puez** group: a set of not-very-accessible peaks overlooking the Passo Gardena and the town of Selva di Gardena, for a total of about 9500 hectares. The Odle group looks like stone fingers, while the Gardenaccia is an arid and inhospitable lunar landscape.

All of this makes the park a low-tourist-density area, to the exception of the Santa Cristina ski district that runs up against the Odle group. The cross-country trails that venture into the Vallunga, into the very heart of the park, are less dis-

Top, the crowded streets of Ortisei and a view of Santa Cristina.
Facing page, the sculptures in wood (generally Swiss pine) of the Val Gardena.

Selva di Val Gardena is located at the end of the valley, almost up against the Sella massif. The spectacle offered by the surrounding mountains is marvelous, with the Sassolungo and the Odle groups that seem about to topple onto the town. Selva is also a strategic point in the Dolomite ski circuit.

From Selva we may ascend to the **Ciampinoi**, the panoramic lookout par excellence of the Val Gardena and one of the most spectacular in all of the Dolomites, with its 360° view taking in both the Sella and the Sassolungo as well as the entire Parco Naturale Puez-Odle above the town of Selva. You can also see much of the Val Gardena, with Santa Cristina and Ortisei almost fused together and surmounted by the wide-open spaces of the Alpe di Siusi behind which are visible the sheer walls of the Sciliar.

MASTERPIECES IN WOOD

*A*mong its many distinctive features, the Val Gardena is famous for its **wooden sculptures**, made mostly of Swiss pine, that are the true masterpieces produced in the respect of a tradition of centuries' standing. It began in the 1600s in Pescosta, a small outlying ward of Ortisei, and by the early 1800s hundreds of valley-dwellers practiced the craft and were selling their wares throu-

of each work are produced with the aid of pantographs. This makes for competitive prices, but by and large the sculptor's shop has succumbed to the factory, as is easy to see in the industrial park at Ortisei.

ghout the world. Today, shops can be found everywhere in the valley, alongside the workshops of the artist-craftsmen. A hallmark guarantees the authenticity of the works. Unfortunately, this craft has today been scaled up to industrial-level and many copies

The Odle group seen from the Passo delle Erbe.

On the following page, a splendid panorama of the Parco Puez-Odle-Gardenaccia, wich the town of Selva, the take-off point for the Vallunga.

turbing to the fauna thanks to the absence of lifts and the generally limited environmental impact of this winter sport.

Along the many well-marked trails for summer hiking you may spot any number of animals, from the **golden eagle** to the **chamois** and the **Alpine marmot**. An absolute must is the **Arco della Stevia**, a spectacular erosion phenomenon with an arch of more than 25 meters.

EVAPORITES

*T*his name applies to a series of sedimentary **rocks** formed by direct precipitation of certain chemical compounds from sea water, following intense evaporation and consequent increase in the saline content.

If we were to allow a pail full of sea water to stand until it had completely evaporated, we would find on the bottom a thin layer of mineral salts, including not only sodium chloride (common table salt) but also many others, like gypsum, anhydrite, various carbonates, etc. In nature, there exist special environments called salines where these salts precipitate spontaneously from sea water. Naturally, this occurs only under certain well-defined conditions: the main requisite is a high rate of evaporation, sufficient to increase the concentration of salts in the water to saturation - at which point they will precipitate. Today, these conditions exist in warm low-lying coastal environments, where there are lagoons, shallow water, and tide flats, the tides rise over vast areas and permit precipitation of large quantities of salts. This happens, for example, in the southern Persian Gulf, where we have the precipitation of gypsum (hydrated calcium sulfate), anhydrite (anhydrous calcium sulfate), and carbonates, among which that mineral known as dolomite. If we were to dig a ditch in such an area, we would discover many layers of the abovementioned compounds, deposited over time.

This particular type of environment, in which highly complex depositional and diagenetic mechanisms come into play, is known to the geologists by the Arab name sabkha. And it is the type of environment that must have been found in the Dolomite region 250 million years ago. We can in fact still admire the beautiful successions of rocks that reflect the more or less cyclical occurrence of the same compounds we would see in our trench on the Persian Gulf. The repetition of these cycles is due, now as then, to periodical oscillations in the level of the sea.

In the Dolomite evaporite succession, as in that of the Persian Gulf today, there is no sodium chloride, the dominant organoleptic of sea water. This fact is easily explained by the high water-solubility of sodium chloride: a brief immersion was sufficient each time to wash away the surface crusts of the mineral.

Examples of evaporite successions: left, a formation at the foot of Monte Seceda in Val Gardena and, right, rocks between Vigo di Fassa and the Passo Costalunga.

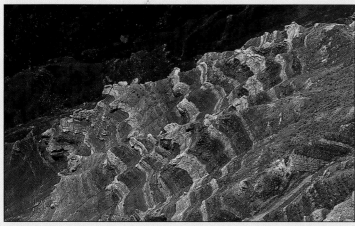

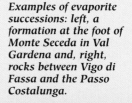

LOCAL COLOR IN THE VAL GARDENA

*D*on't miss the Gardena folk festival on the first Sunday in August, with a parade, local bands, and the traditional costumes of the various towns in the valley, in a true explosion of colors. The costumes are patent evidence of the Tyrolean origin of the people of this area.

The first Sunday in September is instead the date of the Giornata Internazionale Escursionistica (International Hiking Day) celebrated here each year.

Excursion

The Vallunga

On the outskirts of Selva is the trail head for an easy walk through the Vallunga, a valley of glacial origin that runs as far as the Rifugio Puez in the heart of the Puez-Odle-Gardenaccia park. The valley is locked in amongst towering mountains with sheer cliff faces: the best known of these is probably the Sella group, on the left, at the base of which are the ruins of a castle that in the Middle Ages was the home of the Wolkenstein family.
Despite the steepness of its sides, the Vallunga is a gentle, almost level plain.

As you climb toward Puez you will see above, almost on the crest, the Arco della Stevia, a natural window 25 meters high and 12 meters wide. It is an impressive example of what can be done by Nature using erosion, of dimensions that are difficult to appreciate from the valley bottom. The Vallunga is a summer haven for many tourists, and in winter the kingdom of cross-country ski enthusiasts.

Left, a closeup of the natural arch on the ridge of the Stevia group (below).

From the top, clockwise: the green pastures of Pra da Ri in Selva di Gardena, rhododendrons in flower in Vallunga, a colorful Campanula rapuncoloides, and lichens of the genus Cladonia, a pioneering flora in these areas.

Excursion

The Alpe di Siusi

A ski district par excellence, this area is perfect in summer for easy but not for this reason any less interesting walks and hikes. There are two ways of reaching the Alpe: either use the Ortisei lift facilities or take the road that passes through Castelrotto to ample parking facilities in the heart of the Alpe massif.

Up here, it is easy to understand why the trails of the Sciliar-Alpe di Siusi park are almost all on the same side. Up close, the Sciliar proves to be a block of solid rock that is accessible only to intrepid climbers. It is difficult to open trails on its slopes, and the majority of tourist activities is concentrated in the grassy upland plains of the Alpe di Siusi.

The area is a botanical paradise only in early spring, since grazing and systematic haymaking have made it a vast lawn in summer: extremely pleasing to the eye, but floristically impoverished. From wherever you arrive, the trails wind through the grassy plateau and are simple, relaxing walks. Buses, taxis, and horse-drawn carriages take the laziest visitors from the parking facilities to the group of hotels at the center of the Alpe.

A chair-lift runs along the Sasso Piatto, one of the three peaks of the Sassolungo group, offering a splendid view of the mountain and indeed the whole Alpe di Siusi.

Above, the green of the pastures of the Alpe di Siusi and the Sciliar. Left, the Rifugio Molignon against the background of the Sassolungo.

On the following pages, the majestic Monte Sciliar in Sciliar-Alpe di Siusi park.

Excursion

The Sassolungo

One of the most peculiar and most easily recognizable rock complexes in all the Dolomites, the Sassolungo is actually made up of three mountains joined like Siamese triplets but each independent of the others. The mountain group overlooks the Passo Sella and offers its best views from Belvedere di Canazei and from the pass itself, where there are lift facilities for ascending the slopes. The group takes its name from the highest mountain, called the Sassolungo ('long rock') simply because it is higher than the others. This mountain is to the right viewed from the Passo Sella, and is separated from the others by a steep scree which in winter is a ski trail by the name of Forcella di Sassolungo. It is one of the most difficult trails, suitable only for expert skiers with perfect sang-froid.

A lift takes you to the peak of the Forcella, and from here a trail spirals down around the mountain, leading back to the Passo Sella after about 3 to 4 hours. The descent is on snow, which in this ravine never melts completely away. At the bottom, a turnoff to the right (trail no. 528) takes you to the Rifugio Comici and from here closes the roundabout to the Passo Sella, your point of departure. The first portion runs under the sheer side of the mountain, but from the Rifugio Comici on you will enjoy one of the most curious and unexpected natural spectacles in the entire Dolomite area: the Città dei Sassi.

Rarely has a name been more appropriate. Immense blocks of stone, like houses both as to size and to shape, often squared-off, are distributed quite uniformly over a grassy plain. This is not the aftermath of a landslide, since the masses are distributed evenly, almost like the houses in a town. The sight is suggestive and the trail, which all things considered is one of the easiest, runs through these blocks as if it were a street. Clinging to the stones by their twisted roots are large exemplars of the Swiss pine tree; the more demanding firs grow in sparse order on the surrounding plain.

From left to right, a view of the Città dei Sassi in winter and summer trekking around the Sassolungo, through a gorge in which snow persists even in August.

The awe-inspiring Sassolungo complex.

heart of the Parco Naturale Fanes-Sennes-Braies. In the Gothic parish **church** of San Vigilio you will find some noteworthy frescoes.

Continuing through the Val Badia, instead, the road runs up a series of steep switchbacks until reaching **La Villa** (in Ladin, 'la Ila'), a ski resort. From here, one road leads through San Cassiano to the Passo del Falzarego and another to the foot of the Sella, where you will find the towns of Corvara and Colfosco.

San Cassiano is a town of Ladin origin, with the name of 'San Cascian'; the language is still spoken by many people here.

Corvara is situated in a wide valley, almost a bowl that forms the upper Val Badia at the foot of the Sasshonger, rising lofty as a pyramid right above the town. Although it is an important tourist center, even the recent buildings in the town have the traditional Tyrolese look.

THE VAL BADIA

If you are coming from the Val Pusteria, your introduction to the Val Badia will be a narrow, shady gorge, cool in summer and always frozen over in winter.

A turnoff leads from Val Badia to a side valley and from here to **San Vigilio-Marebbe**, a small Ladin town. The road continues on into the very

Top, a view of San Cassiano in winter and, right, the town of Colfosco at the foot of the Sella. The large photograph shows the scenario of the upper Val Badia with the town of Corvara at the foot of the Sassongher and, on the left in the background, the town of Colfosco.

The nearby and slightly more elevated **Colfosco** still has many vintage houses and a few *masi*. Corvara and Colfosco are in the very heart of the Dolomites and thus excellent points of departure for excursions.

THE VALLE DI BRAIES AND ITS LAKE

The first impression we receive of this seemingly endless valley as we enter its mouth from the Val Pusteria is one of the most pleasant imaginable. The wooden houses, with their balconies decorated with flowers of every color, seem to be suspended over the high pastures, as green as they are inclined. The taste in decoration, clearly Tyrolean, here reaches its maximum heights, with infinite postcard views. A perfect example is the little town of **Ferrara** (Schmieden), surrounded by wooden houses and lawns that form a congenially harmonious picture.

The **Lago di Braies**, where the road ends, is felt by many to be the most beautiful lake in the Dolomites, with rock walls that literally fall into the bottle-green water. Do not miss the walk around the lake, which is beautiful and accessible to anyone. The best time of day is in the early morning, when **Croda del Becco** is illuminated by the sun and reflected in the lake; on a cloudless day the whole image is magnificent. In the afternoon, the mountain is backlit and the chromatic effect diminishes.

Views of the Val di Braies: top, some homes near the little town of Ferrara (center), and the Lago di Braies, one of the area's greatest tourist draws.

93

PARCO NATURALE FANES-SENNES-BRAIES, PARCO DELLE DOLOMITI DI SESTO, PARCO REGIONALE NATURALE D'AMPEZZO

These three natural parks embrace the territories of the Dolomites of Sesto, Fanes-Sennes-Braies, and Ampezzo, and extend for over 25,000 hectares of territory the first and about 11,000 hectares each the second and the third. Three areas, with different names and administrations, but all contiguous and all morphologically similar, that are all part of a single large territory north of Cortina that comprises all the most important mountains: **Tofane**, **Cristallo**, **Fanes**, **Sennes**, **Sasso della Croce**, **Croda Rossa**, **Croda del Becco**, and the **Tre Cime di Lavaredo**. Peaks all, excepting the area with the ski trails, which all things considered are trifles with respect to the rest. The Fanes-Sennes-Braies and Dolomiti di Sesto parks lie entirely within the territory administered by Bolzano (their southern limit is in fact the boundary of the Regione Veneto), and to the north they extend almost to Brunico and Dobbiaco in Val Pusteria. They are divid-

Dwarf pines attempt to colonize the wide scree that covers half the slope of the Furcia dai Fers in the Parco Naturale Fanes-Sennes-Braies. Right, one of the small lakes near the Passo del Limo, with the Sasso della Croce in the background.

Excursion

Parco Naturale Fanes-Sennes-Braies

You will need your own transportation to cover the 12 kilometers of toll road that from San Vigilio-Marebbe lead into the heart of the park through a splendid wood of Scotch pine to the Rifugio Pederù with its capacious parking facilities. From here you may proceed on foot or profit by a jeep service in either of the two principal directions. Since the scheduling is limited both as to time and number of trips, it is a good idea to arrive early so as not to risk being left grounded.

The road leading to the Rifugio Sennes is extremely steep, in some stretches exceeding 40% slope. From the Rifugio Sennes, trail no. 6 and a couple of hours take you to the Rifugio Biella for a breather before you tackle the last lap to the Croda del Becco crest. It is worth the climb, since from the top the panorama over Lago di Braies is magnificent. We

recommend starting out early, since from departure to arrival this excursion will take up the whole day. The road in the other direction, leading to the Rifugio Fanes, is a gentler climb to a point near the Sasso della Croce. It is a less difficult way of making what may well be a more complete acquaintance with the park. Not far away is the Rifugio Lavarella, situated in a wetland area with small irregular-shaped lakes and surrounded by stratified rocks that are a geologist's paradise. This is the center of the Sasso della Croce, a tormented arrangement white rock in castle formations and sharp spires that lend the area a lunar cast.

From the Rifugio Fanes, an easy trail sets out for the Passo Limo (about half an hour) in the lee of the Alpe di Fanes Grande, with two small lakes. From the slope, a glance in the direction of the valley behind reveals

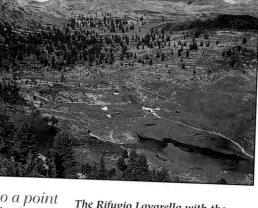

The Rifugio Lavarella with the Lago Verde, in a broad basin of glacial origin. Below, the Furcia dai Fers.

the Rifugio Pederù and the immense screes of the Sella di Fanes and the Furcia dai Fers in the foreground, while behind towers the massif of the Alpe di Sennes.

Just past the pass there opens a superb panorama of the Tofane group and the sharply-cut gorge of the Valle di Fanes, with in the distance the impressive rocky steeples of the Cristallo massif that overlooks Cortina d'Ampezzo.

The profile of the Croda del Becco that reflects in the waters of the Lago di Braies.

ed only by the Dobbiaco-Cortina road. The Parco Regionale Naturale d'Ampezzo begins at the Regione Veneto border, or, more precisely, at the border between the Provincia di Belluno and the Provincia di Bolzano; it extends south to include another important series of mountains. Together, the three parks cover the entire northeastern portion of the Dolomites.

The Parco Naturale Fanes-Sennes-Braies, founded in 1980, and that of the Dolomiti di Sesto, founded a year later, are managed by the Provincia di Bolzano, but the Parco Regionale Naturale d'Ampezzo is managed by a private body, the Co-

munanza delle Regole d'Ampezzo, which for centuries has been the *de facto* authority in these mountains.

All this may seem ridiculous to the tourist, who sees the three parks, with a road on one side and an administrative boundary on the other, for what they really are. Since these divisions are non-existent in nature, what we actually have is one huge protected area of about 50,000 hectares with fairly uniform botanical and faunistic characteristics, no matter what the administrators might think.

Most of the territory lies at more than 2000 meters altitude; it is mostly barren and rocky terrain with a belt of woods and pastures all around. Most of it is accessible only on foot, but the trails are well marked. Together, the three parks represent the largest protected area in the Dolomite region and are home to many animals and plants in a practically intact habitat.

THE VALLE DI LANDRO

This valley divides the Fanes-Sennes-Braies park from that of the Dolomiti di Sesto.

The valley itself is not particularly interesting, unless we count some beautiful views.

A little before reaching **Lago di Landro**, a small parking area on the left of the road offers a lovely panorama of the Tre Cime di Lavaredo group

through the 'V' of the mouth of the Rienza river valley. But the best lies ahead: the lake is a restful oasis with low shores covered with vegetation in many places. Its clear waters reflect one of the best faces of the Cristallo group, the peak of which is often snow-capped even in summer. This view is best in the morning, since in the afternoon the sun is behind the mountain.

The unmistakable brick-red peak of the Croda Rossa looms on the right a little further ahead.

Top, the Cristallo group and a view of the Lago di Landro; center and bottom, the uniquely-colored Croda Rossa.

A view of the Lago di Carezza, one of the most charming sites in these valleys.

THE VALLE D'EGA

This narrow valley is an outcrop of the Dolomites of Bolzano that has insinuated itself into the territory of Trento.

It runs through one of the Dolomites' most spectacular gorges to link the city of Bolzano with the Val di Fassa. The road was to all effects cut into the porphyry walls of the gorge by the torrent, with its perennially white-capped waters, that races along the bottom. In winter, enormous columns of ice plummet vertically from the walls, which are shaded for most of the day, in a spectacle of transparent lace.

There are no particularly important centers in the valley, and the road continues through the woods to the **Lago di Carezza**, one of the most suggestive of the Dolomite lakes. The image is a classic, with greenish waters reflecting the stark rocky spires of the **Latemar** organ-pipes formation. The name 'Carezza' is the Italian adaptation of the dialectical term (*carice*) for the species of palustrine sedge that inhabits the lake.

The Passo di Costalunga takes us into the Dolomites of Trento.

THE VOLCANIC DOLOMITES

About 270 million years ago, the western portion of the Dolomite territory was theater to major volcanic activity. Its products are still found in great abundance and extend to the greatest depths in the area between Trento and Bolzano. Near the volcanic landforms still present in the

Dolomite area there formed vents from which issued lava and gas at a temperature of about 1100°C. These masses, made up of enormous quantities of material, slid down toward the valleys on the steepest slopes, like lava flows, at incredibly high speeds, destroying every form of life as they passed. Events of this type generally generate flow speeds of between 60 and 300 kilome-

Val d'Ega. The porphyry cubes used as paving stones and a detail of a natural outcrop of quartziferous porphyry. Below, the roughly spherical outcrops called 'pillow lava' on the Alpe di Siusi are the result of underwater eruptions that occurred more than 200 million years ago.

outcrops of igneous rock bear mute witness to this period. Near Predazzo and the Monzoni group are the remains of what were probably the two major volcanic landforms.

Before reaching the surface, the magma remained for more or less lengthy periods in 'magma chambers' deep within the earth's crust; the same phenomenon occurs today, for example, at Mount Etna. Magma issuing forth on the surface gave rise to effusive rocks; if, instead, it cooled in the magma chambers, it gave rise to enormous bodies of rock called igneous intrusives or plutons. What we see today near Predazzo and the Monzoni mountains are in fact parts of the plutons of

ters per hour over distances of up to 100 kilometers.

This terrifying phenomenon, called the *nuée ardente*, has fortunately occurred only rarely in historical times. One example is the *nuée ardente* that developed during the eruption of Mount Katmai, in 1912 in Alaska, fortunately in a sparsely-populated area: an entire valley of about 130 square kilometers was submerged by a mass of material estimated at about 11 cubic kilometers.

A second volcanic phase occurred in the Dolomites about 232 million years ago. In this period, the region was probably the most important in Europe for volcanism. Today, scattered

the two volcanic apparatuses that once towered over the Dolomites. As these magmatic bodies were cooling inside the magma chambers, they 'cooked' the surrounding rocks at very high temperatures. These contact metamorphic aureoles,

the result of significant chemical and physical transformations (metamorphism) triggered by the cooling plutons, contain some of the most beautiful minerals in the entire Dolomite region.

If the magma reached the surface, the characteristic products of volcanic activity were likely to form. Generally, when we think of an erupting volcano, we picture a whole series of phenomena that take place in the atmosphere. But what happens when an eruption occurs below sea level? The pillow lavas that we see in the Dolomite area are a typical product of undersea eruptions. They are irregular spheroidal bodies lying one next to the other that result from an accumulation of blocks of not-yet consolidated lava at the foot of the undersea volcanoes. These blocks solidified from the outside, where they were in contact with the sea water, while the center remained molten and under pressure. Therefore, the blocks developed the typical 'pillow' or 'grain sack' shape and only then did they solidify completely. These phenomena still occur today at the foot of the mid-oceanic ridges.

Outcrops of 'pillow lava', rocks that are glassy on the outside as a result of the rapid cooling of magma in contact with sea water.

Facing page, the little town of Siusi and the Sciliar group that looms above it - without a doubt one of the most suggestive spectacles in the Dolomites of Bolzano.

Between the deposition one block of lava and the next, sufficient time could pass to allow a layer of sedimentary material to deposit; this is why we find sedimentary rock between the igneous blocks. What is more, the rapid cooling of the outside of these blocks of lava in contact with the sea water formed a sort of glassy crust that when it shattered formed the fragments that can sometimes be seen in the interstices between the 'pillows'.

THE VENETIAN DOLOMITES

These mountains extend from the Piave to the border with the Dolomites of Bolzano and of Trento. The political boundary between the Regione Trentino-Alto Adige and the Regione Veneto often cuts entire mountains in two.

This is the case with the Pale di San Martino and the Marmolada, but more frequently it has been the mountains that have divided the two populations.

The Venetian Dolomite culture is less mountain-oriented than that of other areas of the Dolomites: the proverbial Venetian hospitality triumphs, as in the plains areas, and the welcome is excellent - Mediterranean, we might say - with something for everyone. In San Cassiano, for instance, the owner of the pensione will greet you cordially and then disappear, convinced he need not address you again all day; in Pecol he will buttonhole you and recount seven generations of family history in pure Venetian dialect. The rest of the service will be impeccable in both cases, however.

German-language tourism is widespread in these mountains and all the tourist operators speak German - but haltingly, as Italian is spoken in Val Badia. It is interesting to note how the tourist to the Dolomites, tends to be Italian or German, while those from other countries are relatively few.

Pieve di Cadore. The house in which Titian was born today hosts a museum dedicated to the great artist, and in the square a monument has been raised in his honor. Facing, the Passo Giau dominated by the peak of the Nuvolau.

THE CADORE AREA

A vast region with nebulous boundaries, that occupies a large part of the Venetian Dolomites and leads out toward the east.

Pieve di Cadore is the best-known town. It stands above the artificial **lake** to which it lends its name, and exhibits traces of an interesting past history. The ancient, richly-decorated capital of Cadore belies the past prosperity of the local merchants, who traded in wood with the Republic of Venice. Cadore is also the birthplace of **Titian**. Everything here recalls the great painter, from the house in which he was born, containing mementos of his life, to the **church** of Santa Maria Nascente, with its paintings, including some by Titian himself, to the pleasant Piazza Tiziano with the

16th-century palace of the Magnifica Comunità di Cadore, and its museum.

Pieve di Cadore is nevertheless located at the extreme limit of the Dolomite territory, while **Santo Stefano di Cadore**, for example, is decidedly outside the mountains on the road to Sappada. At the other extreme is **Selva di Cadore**, in the heart of the Dolomites, at about the halfway point between Cortina and the Marmolada. It is a center for tourism, with its 15th-century Gothic church of

Right, the old Piazza Tiziano and the Palace of the Magnifica Comunità of Cadore in Pieve di Cadore.

THE PAST, TODAY

Among these valleys and mountains there are two **architectural styles** of note: that of the large centers, such as Cortina d'Ampezzo, which has mostly given way to modern architecture, and that of the small valleys, where the tendency is to preserve the old homes and constructions in stone and wood. The Val di Zoldo and the Val Fiorentina, like the Falcade, are in this sense a true leap into the past and in no way inferior to the architecture of Val Badia. The old homes are often partially in masonry with an upper story in wood; the inlaid decoration is often noteworthy even when the building is a simple barn or stable.

Top and right center, two examples of the traditional wooden shelters called stàvoli in Pecol di Zoldo; left center, a detail of the ancient construction technique still put to good use today; bottom, a traditional building in Pescul.

San Lorenzo.

All the roads running through the southeastern part of the Dolomites thus also run through the **Cadore** region, of which the **Val d'Ansiei** and the **Valle d'Ampezzo** are the most typical valley.

DELIGHTFUL FLAVORS

*T*he **cuisine** here is the least mountain-style in all the Dolomites, since it is greatly influenced by Venetian cooking, traditionally much more delicate than that of either Trento or the Alto Adige. Polenta reigns supreme, with various sauces, from the osei al capriolo *to mountain game or Luganega sausage, which is often highly-flavored as are*

many other of the pork-butcher's wares. The gnocchi Cadore-style *are excellent, whether green or cheese-filled. The first courses prepared using local vegetables are an on-going tradition and often vary greatly from valley to valley. For example, there is a*

very tasty kind of ravioli (casunzei) *that may be filled with turnip greens, beet greens, spinach, or other vegetables and are often served with a simple sauce of melted butter and cheese. The barley soup is another typical dish, as are the local head cheeses and their relatives*

the ossocolli, *or the speck roasted in a hollowed-out loaf of bread. The pork hock is perhaps less common than it is in Trentino, but is not a rarity; the cold cuts and cheeses are good but less typical. The liquors are those you find in the other areas, although in proportion the grappas are more numerous.*

THE MARMAROLE, THE ANTELAO, AND THE SORAPIS

These are the main mountains of the Cadore area and are separated from the parks (Fanes-Sennes-Braies, Dolomiti di Sesto, and Ampezzo) only by the eastern ski area of Cortina. Despite this, the flora and the fauna are basically the same, and in this case as well we have a *de facto* park situa- tion, since these peaks are difficult both to reach and to scale.

The glacial circle of the **Sorapis** is splendid, as is the state-owned Somadida forest in the **Val d'Ansiei** on the north slopes of the Marmarole.

A breathtaking view from the Antelao: the Oten valley and the Marmarole.

Above, the sharp peak of the Antelao, often snow-capped even in summer, and, below, the irregular profile of the Marmarole seen from the Val d'Ansiei. The extremely harsh terrain of these mountains is almost impenetrable, so much so that the majority of the territory has never been explored.

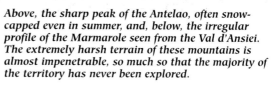

THE VAL D'ANSIEI

This valley opens out from the Piave valley and thrusts in among the Dolomiti di Sesto and the vast Marmarole group that for almost the entire length of the road dominate on the left.

A few kilometers up the valley is the long, narrow artificial **Lago di Santa Caterina**, with on its shores the town of **Auronzo**. To say that the town makes its living from the lake is not quite exact, but neither is it completely wrong. Tourism centers on the lake, with its beaches and pedal boats on cobalt-green water, ringed by mountains: the Aiarnola, the Croda di Ligonto, the Dodici peak and, in the background, the Tre Cime di Lavaredo with a clear view of the saddle on which the Rifugio Auronzo nestles. Probably the best view ever of the Parco delle Dolomiti di Sesto.

As we go on we begin to see the different **Croda** peaks on the right, while the **Marmarole** group stands alone on the other side. Under the Marmarole, kilometer after kilometer, the firs dominate and grow more majestic until we find ourselves in the Somadida forest, from which for centuries the Republic of Venice cut the wood used to build its fleet.

After the forest, the valley narrows and on the left, instead of the Marmarole, we now see the stately **Sorapis** and **Cristallo** groups, while the curve takes us almost all around the **Cadini** group on the other side. The best time of day for seeing these mountains is early morning, because later the sun is behind the Sorapis and the glacier is hardly visible. The valley ends at the **Lago di Misurina**, of which the Ansiei river is emissary.

The lake, despite its well-deserved fame as the mirror of the Tre Cime di Lavaredo, one of the

The town of Auronzo on the artificial Lago di Santa Caterina. In the background, the Dolomiti di Sesto.

best known groups in the Dolomites, is probably best seen from the other side in the early morning, when the Sorapis is illuminated by the sun and its reflection in the lake possesses a majesty unrivaled by the farther-off Tre Cime.

The lake is surrounded by hotels, parking facilities and benches, and, aside from its eastern side into which the vertical walls of the Cadini literally 'fall', has lost much of that simplicity that characterizes the other Dolomite lakes.

THE VALLE D'AMPEZZO

The valley begins a short way south of Pieve di Cadore, in the Piave valley, and in its first part is narrow and not overly panoramic. Only further up does it become wider and sunny, with Cortina d'Ampezzo, your point of arrival.

The mountains that dominate the panorama (weather permitting) are the sharply-pointed peak of the **Antelao** on the right and the hulking **Pelmo** on the left. Further ahead the Antelao yields to the **Sorapis**, of which we see the opposite side from that we see from the Val d'Ansiei, and the Pelmo to the **Croda da Lago**.

The Cristallo, belted by fir-woods, seen from the Val d'Ansiei and, below, the Lago di Misurina in the unequaled setting provided by the massive Sorapis group.

Above, the Marmarole and the Dolomiti di Sesto from the northeast slope of the Antelao; left, the Sorapis complex seen from the meadows of the Val d'Ampezzo. Facing page, the Cima del Bel Prà, the Croda Marcora, and the Punta Sorapis of the Antelao group.

On these two pages, from the top clockwise: the parish church of San Vito di Cadore with the Punta Nera in the background; the Rifugio San Marco and the access to the Sorapis; Cortina, in the shadow of the Sorapis and the Antelao, seen from the Tofane; tourists in Corso Italia; a view of Cortina from the Tofane cableway.

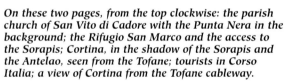

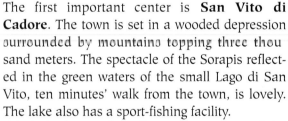

The first important center is **San Vito di Cadore**. The town is set in a wooded depression surrounded by mountains topping three thousand meters. The spectacle of the Sorapis reflected in the green waters of the small Lago di San Vito, ten minutes' walk from the town, is lovely. The lake also has a sport-fishing facility.

A little further on the valley widens again and the road passes through a beautiful Scotch pine woods, while in the background the Tofane begin to make their appearance. As soon as you begin to have a clear view of the Cristallo group as well, you know you have reached the broad bowl of **Cortina d'Ampezzo**, the most resort in the entire Dolomite region.

Cortina is set in a felicitous position among mountains of undoubted aesthetic value. It is nicknamed the 'Pearl of the Dolomites' and is in

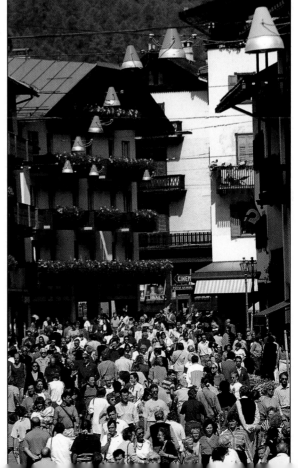

The mid-19th century bell tower of the Baroque parish church of Cortina thrusts upward against the backdrop of the Col Rosà. Below, a sculpture exhibited at one of the town's many shows.

truth the perfect spot for those who, although they want to spend their vacation time in the mountains, do not want to do without social life, evening entertainment, and shopping. The town has grown out of all proportion, with the homes of the residents, the summer homes, and the hotels, and is now far and away the most populous of the centers in the Dolomite region. **Corso Italia**, closed to automobile traffic, is the most elegant promenade with shops of every type, from the bargain basement to all the great-name boutiques. Nor is there any lack of historical and artistic sights, like the **Ciasa delle Regole** with its group of theme museums, including an excellent geological exhibit.

The 'Regole' is a sort of herding and pastoral consortium of Lombard origin, composed of about eight hundred heads of family of the ancient Ampezzo line, known as the *Regolieri*. This association has been administering the valley for centuries on the basis of the commonage of the *maso*, the pastures, and the woods of the area, which although individually owned are used by all members of the community.

Of note is the 18th-century **parochial church** of

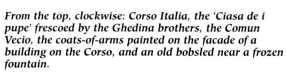

From the top, clockwise: Corso Italia, the 'Ciasa de i pupe' frescoed by the Ghedina brothers, the Comun Vecio, the coats-of-arms painted on the facade of a building on the Corso, and an old bobsled near a frozen fountain.

117

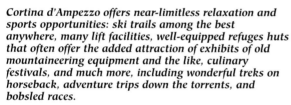

Cortina d'Ampezzo offers near-limitless relaxation and sports opportunities: ski trails among the best anywhere, many lift facilities, well-equipped refuges huts that often offer the added attraction of exhibits of old mountaineering equipment and the like, culinary festivals, and much more, including wonderful treks on horseback, adventure trips down the torrents, and bobsled races.

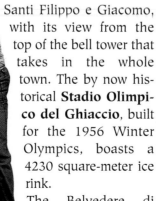

Santi Filippo e Giacomo, with its view from the top of the bell tower that takes in the whole town. The by now historical **Stadio Olimpico del Ghiaccio**, built for the 1956 Winter Olympics, boasts a 4230 square-meter ice rink.

The Belvedere di Pocol lookout, on the road to the Passo del Falzarego, offers a fine view of the city, but the best panorama of all is probably that from the **Ra Valles**, the second spur of the Tofane, accessible by cableway. From the panoramic terrace of the refuge you can see the Cortina valley closed in as though in a frame by the **Pomagagnon**, beyond which looms the Cristallo massif on the left and the Sorapis and the Antelao ahead and slightly to the right. Further right yet are the harsh natural buttresses of the Croda da Lago, flanked by the **Nuvolau**, obscuring the Pelmo. Behind are the steep walls of the Tofane with their bands of stratifications.

them with the aid of a map is an amusing pastime.

Since the lifts and the panoramic lookouts are musts for getting to know the Dolomites, you shouldn't miss a trip to the nearby **Passo del Falzarego** on the Lagazuoi cableway. Besides a great view of the three Tofane peaks (that, however, hide the mountains to the north), the pass offers the best panorama of all over the southern Dolomites. From left to right are the Sorapis, the Antelao, the Pelmo, the Croda da Lago, the Cinque Torri, the Averau, the Civetta, the Pale di San Martino, the Marmolada with its glacier, and finally the Sella massif. The best time of day is early morning, when the air is clearest, or in the late afternoon to enjoy the best light.

If you descend from the panoramic terrace and cross to the other side, beyond the lifts, you will discover a pleasing new outlook on the **Croda del Becco** and the **Croda Rossa**, the latter with its unmistakable color. On a clear day, other peaks appear in the background; identifying

The terrace of the Rifugio Ra Valles, above, and the panorama of the Venetian Dolomites from the Lagazuoi: in the distance, Monte Pelmo and the Civetta.
Facing page, the Averau seen from the Lagazuoi.

120

Above, two images of the Pomagagnon (with the Cristallo visible above).
Right, the irregular spires of the Cime di Fanis seen from the Lagazuoi and, bottom,
the unmistakable colors of the Croda Rossa that stand out against the other rocks.

The Tre Cime di Lavaredo

From the Lago di Misurina, a panoramic toll road leads to the Rifugio Auronzo, with ample parking facilities for cars, buses and campers.
This refuge is the starting point for the excursion around the Tre Cime di Lavaredo, one of the 'classical' mountain groups and one that can be seen only at the cost of a hike, even though the trail is accessible to everyone. We recommend proceeding counterclockwise in order to enjoy the best light. The excursion lasts 3 to 4 hours, with a loop into the Parco delle Dolomiti di Sesto in the Provincia di Bolzano - but this is only an administrative oddity.

The first stretch, up to the Rifugio Lavaredo, is an old army road that is easy to walk. From Lavaredo, three different routes branch off for the Rifugio Locatelli, in a sense the omphalos of the Parco delle Dolomiti di Sesto. The lower trail, no. 101, is easy and can be hiked by anyone; the intermediate trail, halfway up a broad scree, requires some attention but is the most panoramic; the highest trail is an equipped path recommended only for experts.

Below, the Rifugio Locatelli against the backdrop of the Torre Tobliner; left, an excursion to the Tre Cime di Lavaredo.

The Tre Cime di Lavaredo, the most famous mountain group in the Dolomiti di Sesto park.

The Rifugio Locatelli is set on a sort of saddle, with views in all directions. Above it is the jagged Monte Paterno, with the amusing 'sausage' (a rock formation) on its crest. On the other side of the saddle, two lakes usher in the view of the Val Sasso Vecchio surrounded by sheer-walled mountains. To the west is the impressive Valle di Rimbon, with walls falling steeply into an extremely narrow gorge. Facing the panoramic terrace of the refuge are the Tre Cime di Lavaredo. Well-separated, absurdly squared off and vertical on this side, they are backlit for most of the day: we recommend planning to spend the night at the refuge in order to see them at sunset, when the sun finally lights them from this side.

Around the refuge there still can be seen fortifications dating to World War I. A stretch of the climber's path passes through a gallery cut at the time, in these mountains where Italians and Austrians fought for each single stone with rivers of blood. The signs of conflict are still visible today, on the rock walls, like unhealed wounds. We return down the easy and well-marked trail no. 105, that flanks the Valle di Rimbon, scales Col di Mezzo, and thus rounds the Tre Cime, to a splendid panoramic view over the Lago di Misurina closed in by the Cristallo on the right and the Cadini on the left. It is only a short distance from here to the Rifugio Auronzo and the end of the excursion.

Left, Monte Paterno and right, a detail of the amusing conformation of its crest.
Below, the Piani lakes, just a short distance from the Rifugio Locatelli.

Above top, a panorama of the Val Fiorentina and,
bottom, Pecol di Zoldo with Monte Pelmo
in the background.
Right, a view of the town of Selva di Cadore.

THE VALLE DI ZOLDO
AND THE VAL FIORENTINA

The ice-cream valley. Thus we might call the Val di Zoldo, since from its towns hundreds of ice-cream makers have set out to take the art of hand-made Italian ice-cream to Germany, Switzerland, Austria, and a goodly part of north-central Italy. Many of these ice-cream makers spend the summer season away from home but return in the winter, when ice-cream is in less demand and the ski tourism industry creates jobs in the towns.

The valley begins as an understatement, leaving Longarone and snaking slowly up along the spurs of the impressive **Schiara** group. Narrow, winding roads, a few artificial lakes. This valley is off the beaten tourist track and in fact, with the exception of the Pecol and Palafavera campsites, there are few beds available. For this reason, and because it is rapidly accessible from the south, the tourist operators count more on weekends than on longer-term stays. But the natural beauty of the valley is in no way inferior to many of the more famous places. The **Civetta** on the one side, the **Pelmo** on the other - and these are among the most spectacular of the Dolomites. The excursions are many, and the ski trails are excellent and well equipped.

On the fringes of the major tourist circuit as it is, the small historical centers in this valley are better preserved than in other localities. The towns of the Val di Zoldo are not rebuilt in period style: they are originals. **Zoldo Alto**, **Mareson**, **Fusine**, **Coi**, and **Pecol** still have their old homes, wooden barns that are still in regular use, and in general an architecture of times past.

The splendid view looking toward Cortina from the Passo di Giau. Left, the Croda da Lago.

tional wooden shelters, the *stàvoli*, bursting with hay and presided over by cows and chickens.

At the end of the Val Fiorentina is the town of **Selva di Cadore**, in the very heart of the Dolomites in the Cadore region. At **Colle Santa Lucia**, three kilometers to the southwest, are a few 17th-century homes.

From Selva di Cadore you may choose to turn off for Colle Santa Lucia, in the direction of the Cordevole valley, or to tackle the hair-raising switchbacks of the **Passo Giau** that leads to Cortina through a fairy-tale landscape of Alpine meadows, with unequaled panoramic views of the **Nuvolau** and **Croda da Lago** mountains.

Past the **Forcella Staulanza**, at the end of the valley, we descend into the Val Fiorentina, where we find more towns, like **Pescul**, that also seem to have stepped out of a history book.

A stimulating contrast is created by the ultra-modern lift facilities standing alongside the tradi-

Excursion

To the Cinque Torri

From the grassy bowl of the pass, over which soar the rock curtain of the Croda da Lago and the sharp peak of the Nuvolau, it is only a short trek to a group that is a 'classic' among the Dolomite formations: the Cinque Torri, or Five Towers.

The route, which makes a closed ring around the Nuvolau, may be traveled clockwise or counterclockwise, but in both cases the point of arrival is the Rifugio Cinque Torri, under these natural monuments that seem almost to be a gigantic locomotive and railroad cars.

If we go counterclockwise, the trail takes us through a series of small ravines with descents and ascents over extremely irregular rocks. The other side is less interesting but more panoramic. The variety of flowers on the slopes of the Nuvolau is amazing: from rock-dwellers to typical meadow flowers as the environments change.

In either direction, the excursion takes from three to four hours.

To tell the truth, it is easier to reach the towers from the Passo del Falzarego, using the lift facilities, but the views from the Passo Giau are well worth the effort of a hike.

From the Passo Giau, Monte Nuvolau with its easy trails and, below, the Cinque Torri group seen from the Passo del Falzarego.

IN THE STEPS OF THE DINOSAURS

On the Pelmetto, the minor massif of Monte Pelmo in the Val di Zoldo, we find rocks that once were nothing but deposits of silt in the shallow waters of swamps already on the way to drying up. On this mud, during the upper Triassic (about 200 million years ago) there walked small dinosaurs between 80 centimeters and three meters in height. Their small size mustn't fool us; they were the progenitors of the enormous animals that were to dominate the world in later epochs. These were smaller only because they were earlier, and this makes the discovery of their tracks even more important and surprising.

Over the millions of years that followed, the mud solidified and stratified into the rock that is today Monte Pelmo and all the surrounding mountains. By a stroke of pure luck, some blocks of rock detached from the wall and one of them stopped its roll down the slope in an ideal position for observation. One cannot but ask oneself what else is hidden in the mountain.

One of the most exceptional facts about this find is that the dinosaur tracks belong to not one but to three different animals, and they are distributed in such a manner as to clearly show the sequence of the steps. Many isolated prints have been found in various places in the world, but sequences are very rare. The advantage of a sequence is that it gives us much important information: for example, if the animal stood on two or four legs, if it ran, if it had a tail, and so on. For calculating the size of the animal, the size of the print and its depth are not always sufficient, and the distance between one print and the next can be very useful. The boulder with the prints attracts attention, with its nearly verti-

1: Coelosauro
2: Ornitisco
3: Prosauropode

The fascinating sequence of fossil dinosaur tracks in what was once muddy soil.

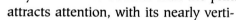

cal line of prints, wich are clearly delineated, with raised borders on account of the mud that was pushed sideways by the weight of the reptile. In order to understand how this animal, a primitive **ornithischian** about 1.5 meters tall, moved, we must first remember that the prints go from top to bottom on the rock. Some larger prints on

130

the lower portion of the rock were produced by another animal, probably a **prosauropod**, a herbivore of about three meters that walked on two legs. On the left side is a series of smaller prints, at first glace jumbled but distinguishable into different series, that have been attributed to **coelosaurs**, small, agile, and fast-moving carnivores no taller than one meter.

To reach the dinosaur prints, leave your car at the Passo Staulanza that divides the Val di Zoldo from the Val Fiorentina, and take trail no. 472 (Alta Via delle Dolomiti - Anello Zoldano) that links the Forcella Staulanza and the Rifugio Venezia. You can't miss it, since a number of signs point the way to the prints, which are visit-

3

ed each year by thousands of tourists.

The climb is not overly difficult, going as it does from 1766 meters at Forcella Staulanza to 1880 meters at the turn-off, after a couple of kilometers through a wood of larches and firs. From the well-marked turnoff a steep gravelly trail leads to the dinosaur rock, a scarce 200 meters above.

Whatever the species that left their prints in the mud, the rock, framed by the Val di Zoldo with the corrugate peaks of the Dolomites of Belluno on the horizon, is possessed of a subtle fascination.

The hurried but deliberate sequence of prints still recalls all the vital force of the animal, its slowing down, perhaps to look around, and its faster gait later: everyday movements that have come down to us after millions of years. This rock changes our way of thinking about time: here was an animal crossing a mud flat as it did every day, but this time its prints were preserved - and in the

meantime the continents were shifting and the look of our planet was changing and continued to change time after time until becoming the habitat we know today.

THE PELMO

This mountain closes the circle around Cortina, which becomes, in practice, an anthropized island at the center of a single great park, even though it is somewhat fragmented. A 1989 law established the importance of safeguarding Monte Pelmo and the adjacent areas, like the Croda da Lago and the nearby Passo Giau. Impressive formations of narrow ledges on the rock face make the area an important open-air geological laboratory; the discovery of dinosaur tracks and the skeleton of a Mesolithic man, called the Mondeval Man, are sufficient reason to warrant protection. The plants and animals found here are as abundant as they are in other areas, but the scientific importance of the area is dictated mainly by its great number of fossil finds.

Below, the gigantic Monte Pelmo at Zoppé di Cadore.

An eloquent image of the valley in which the Lago di Misurina is set; below, a view of the snow-covered Marmolada glacier. Facing page, a view of the Sassolungo and of the Sassopiatto, from the Marmolada.

DOLOMITES AND GLACIERS

When we mention glaciers, we immediately think of the enormous masses, more or less white in color, that we often imagine being static and immobile. Rarely do we ask ourselves where they come from and where their ice will end up. The glacier is to all effects a moving mass, with an income of mass on one side and an outgo on the other. The term **accumulation** refers more properly to the increase of mass above the equilibrium line, and **ablation** to loss of mass by any means. In detail, a glacier grows by the progressive accumulation of snow, which due to its weight compacts and recrystallizes to form perennial ice. The so-called creep properties of the ice permit the glacier to move, however slowly.

The Alpine glaciers, for example, move at speeds between 100 and 200 meters per year. This continual movement, together with the enormous pressures at the point of contact of the ice with the rocky substrate, remove fragments of rock of various types and sizes from the glacier beds. These fragments are then transported by the glacier itself to great distances. We thus see areas of glacial erosion and other areas in which the eroded and transported fragments are deposited and accumulated.

In the most recent geological past (up to about 15,000 years ago) the Dolomite area was covered by enormous glacial masses that modeled the countryside. The results of their work are the erosional landforms and the accumulation landforms that we see today, even though they have all been more or less touched up by successive processes. We can imagine that at that time,

when there were three times as many glaciers as there are today, the Dolomites were peaks emerging from colossal masses of ice, often well over a thousand meters deep. The ice occupied all the Dolomite valleys and sculpted them with their movement. Thus, for example, many of the valleys have the classical "U" profile typical of the glacial troughs.

Other very interesting forms are the **moraines**. Broadly, a moraine is any type of glacial deposit formed underneath, alongside, or ahead of a moving glacial mass. The accumulated material (called glacial debris or till) is chaotic, and we note materials of all different kinds, from enormous blocks to pebbles, gravel, sand, and mud. The finer materials formed through wear during the movement of the glacier; the pebbles are often faceted, with rounded edges, and may be striated. The so-called **moraine arcs** are also frequent phenomena that typically take the form of an amphitheater. They were created on the leading edges of the glaciers, where the moving mass acted

The 'U' shape of the Valle d'Ampezzo belies how it was modeled by the action of an enormous glacier that millions of years ago covered the entire area.

Above, a 'group photograph'. From left to right, the Cristallo, Sorapis, and Antelao groups, Bec Mezdì, and the Croda da Lago. Right, the morain of the Sorapis' western glacier.

On the following pages, a magical sunset on one of the peaks of the Croda da Lago.

rather like a bulldozer. Many of the moraines in the Dolomites created dams that cut off the flow of water. This is how many of the Dolomite **lakes** were formed: **Carezza**, **Misurina**, and **Braies** are but three examples.

The enormous pressure created by the weight of the ice, on the rock, together with the movement of the glacier, also caused abrasion and scouring of the rock; if we look closely, the signs of glacial action are still visible today. Another characteristic of glacial morphology are the so-called 'cirques'. These are niches in the sides of the mountains just below the crest, dug out in the income zone of the glacier.

Today, there are only ten or so small glaciers in the Dolomites; they are the by now impotent remains of a past in which the glaciers reigned supreme in the entire region.

135

LOOKING FOR MUSHROOMS IN THE DOLOMITES

In the mountains, the period of maximum vitality from the botanical point of view is summer; likewise, mushrooms sprout here only in the warmest weather. July-August is also the period of greatest tourist inflow to the region, and so the Dolomites become singular 'hunting' grounds.

Mushrooms belong to two important subgroups, according to their ecological function: the saprophytes and the symbiotes. The former are the disintegrators of organic substances, from old stumps to dead leaves to

For this reason, the Dolomite mushrooms, or at least the best-known of the symbiotes, are almost exclusively species that rely on the conifers.

The much sought-after *porcino* (*Boletus edulis*, *B. reticolatus*, *B. aureus*, *B. pinicola*) prefers the broadleafs and grows in quantity only in the valley-bottom beechwoods, which are found only on the gentler slopes with the best exposure. The *porcini* of the Dolomites of Trento and Venice are nevertheless those most commonly found on any Italian

1

based here. In the city and the surrounding area, the number of species offered for sale is greater than on any other Italian market, and this is reflected in a diffuse acculturation and the gastronomical tradition.

Among the most commonly-gathered Dolomite mushrooms are the milk-caps (*Lactarius deliciosus*, *L. salmonicolor*, *L. sanguifluus*, *L. semisanguifluus*, and others), which are all edible, conifer-symbiotic species that are easily recognizable because when broken they free a red latex instead of the white or yellow of the toxic species.

The *Amanita rubescens*, a familiar species in the Norway spruce woods, has a delicate flavor and a cap dotted with 'warts'. Attention: it is easily confused with the poisonous *Amanita pantherina*, also found in those woods. The 'good' species is nevertheless rosier in color,

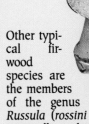

2

Other typical firwood species are the members of the genus *Russula* (*rossini* or *rosselle*, as they are called here). *R. paludosa* and *R. decolorans* are typical of the Dolomite area, since they live among the Alpine blueberry plants.

The *Boletus elegans* grows under the larches; hence its common Italian name *laricino*. It is good eating, and quite common in the Dolomites. The *Boletus tridentinus*, another larch symbiote, is typical of the Dolomites of Trento, hence the species name.

The Swiss pine also has its

3

market during the summer season, thanks to the fact that these woods always retain a certain degree of humidity and abundant growth is therefore assured.

The variety of mushrooms in these mountains is so

5

and if the stem is scratched with a fingernail the 'wound' turns red, while that of the toxic species remains white. The fir-woods also host the spectacular *Amanita muscaria* that we often see in fairy tales and cartoons. The red cap dotted with white is unmistakable, and this is an advantage, since despite its lovely coloration it is very poisonous and to be avoided at all costs.

4

animal excrements. The latter live in symbiosis (a relationship of reciprocal utility) with host plants, generally trees.

great that Trento has become the mycological capital of Italy, with the most important sector publications and associations

6

1   *Boletus elegans*
2   *Amanita rubescens*
3   *Boletus tridentinus*
4   *Boletus edulis*
5   *Amanita pantherina*
6   *Amanita muscaria*
7   *Cantharellus clavatum*

7

8

favorite mushrooms: the *Boletus plorans* and *Boletus placidus*, two lesser-known species. The *Gomphidius helveticus*, also linked to the Swiss pine and the Norway spruce, is a widespread edible species in the Dolomites, but its flavor is nothing special.

Both the very well-known *Cantharellus cibarius* and the fleshy *C. clavatum*, with its violet shadings and slightly bitter taste, are also quite common.

The link with the host plant is not always a positive affair; in some cases the mushroom draws sustenance without giving anything in exchange. The mushroom in this case is a parasite, even though only rarely is it so damaging as to attack healthy trees and lead to their death.

The Dolomite saprophytes are many, like the *Marasmius perforans*, a minuscule fungus that invades the beds of fallen needles in fir-woods and facilitates disintegration: one tiny mushroom for each needle. Many other fungi occupy the same habitat, and thus we often see underwoods put on a chromatic show with spots of color that go from red to white to violet.

Whatever your expertise as a mushroom seeker, it is always advisable to take your finds ti a classification center and ask the opinion of an expert. We also recommend requesting information on the gathering limits, which in some areas are particularly severe.

In the Trentino area, daily, weekly, or monthly permits are issued; the cost varies with the town or district. Two kilograms is generally the daily limit, but in some areas gathering is forbidden altogether.

The restrictions in Alto Adige are more severe: the usual two kilograms per day but with daily permits granted only for even-numbered days.

In the Venetian Dolomites, the overall number of permits is limited. Permits are issued by the Comunità Montana (as well as by the towns and the Provincia). Different limits are set for each species, and the total daily limit is three kilograms.

> **REMEMBER:**
> **NOT ALL MUSHROOMS**
> **ARE EDIBLE !**

8 *Mycena vitilis*
9 *Lactarius salmonicolor*
10 *Gomphidius helveticus*
11 *Russula paludosa*
12 *Marasmius foetidus*
13 *Lactarius deliciosus*

9

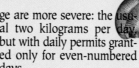

10

11

12

13

Listed below are some of the centers that can provide reliable classification of the mushrooms you have picked.

Gruppo Micologico G. Bresadola di Trento - Museo Tridentino di Scienze Naturali - C.P. 393 - 38100 Trento

Associazione Micologica Bresadola - Via A. Volta, 46 - 38100 Trento

Gruppo Belluno- Istituto Salesiano 'Agosti' - Piazza S. G. Bosco, 12 - 32100 Belluno

Gruppo Bolzano - Scuola Ada Negri - Via Druso, 289, 39100 Bolzano

Gruppo Brunico - Via Europa 8/C - 39031 Brunico (BZ)

Gruppo Daone - Via Lunga, 33 - 38080 Daone (TN)

Gruppo Micologico Naturalistico - Via Pietralba, 37 - 39055 Laives (BZ)

Gruppo 'B. Cetto' - Via Monsignor Caproni, 42 - 38056 Levico (TN)

Gruppo 'Ettore Bettini' - Via 3 November, 2 - 38057 Pergine (TN)

On the left, from top to bottom, a view of Agordo and the harsh slopes of the Pale di San Lucano. Above, the town of Falcade and the Passo del Pellegrino.

VAL DEL CORDEVOLE

Starting out from Belluno, through the first portion of the Parco Nazionale delle Dolomiti Bellunesi, you soon come to **Agordo**, the first town outside the park boundaries, set against the backdrop of the Pale di San Lucano and of Monte Agnèr. The town was once an iron-mining center that supplied the swordsmiths of Belluno and the mint of the Republic of Venice; the town is also famous for its tradition of eyeglass manufacture.

Be sure not to miss the **Crotta Palace** in the main square, or the collection of antique eyeglasses in the former stables, where more than a thousand pieces of various eras are on exhibit.

Since the view of the **Pale di San Lucano** from the road is not the best one, it is worthwhile turning off at Taibòn and following the signs for the

Valle di San Lucano, wild and woods-locked. The narrow, winding road runs alongside a crystal-clear torrent, the Tegnàs, over which the Pale di San Lucano loom almost vertically. The back of the Pale di San Martino crowns the valley, framing it as if in a postcard.

Further up the Cordevole we come to a fork: one road leads to Falcade, and from there to the Passo di San Pellegrino and then to the Val di Fassa; the other takes us to Alleghe, on the lake of the same name.

Falcade is a well-known tourist locality that is equipped for both summer and winter tourism, in the Tre Valli ski district. The historical center boasts many excellently-preserved houses in traditional style. The hamlet of Falcade Alta is lovely, and in a lovely position. It is here that on the first Sunday after Easter the **Pizolada**, a Alpine ski doubles contest, is held. The 12th-century

A panoramic view of the Lago di Alleghe. Still visible are the signs of the slide that created the lake more than two centuries ago.

church of San Simon, a few kilometers from Falcade toward the Cordevole valley, is decorated with frescoes by Paris Bordone (1538); the opening hours are posted.

The other road leads to **Alleghe**. In 1771, a landslide detached from Monte Piz obstructed the course of the Cordevole and created a lake of no small size, which about two centuries has made the fortune of the inhabitants of the town on its shores. In memory of the natural catastrophe, the 18th-century **parochial church** preserves the processional lanterns donated by the Republic of Venice immediately after the destruction of the earlier church by the landslide.

Besides being able to count on the ski season, thanks to the landslide the town also makes its livelihood from the many tourists that flock to the **lake** during the summer. Some sandy areas on the shores have become true mountain beaches; the lake offers vacations for all tastes, with swimming in the shade of the Civetta, the mountain that overlooks the town.

The **Civetta** ('Owl') is the symbol of Alleghe, more even, perhaps, than of the lake. Although the slopes on the Zoldo side are gentle, on this side we find one of the most inaccessible of the vertical Dolomite rock walls, a true challenge for even the most accomplished alpinists - so much so that at one time it was classified as 'impossible'. And observing it from the lake, with your neck twisted to see to the top, does arouse a certain sense of apprehension.

PARCO NAZIONALE DELLE DOLOMITI BELLUNESI

The Parco Nazionale delle Dolomiti Bellunesi, just outside Belluno, lies entirely within the province of the same name and is the most important protected area in all of the Dolomites. The park, in the form of an upside-down bottle, widest in the Sciara massif and narrowing through the Monti del Sole to a 'neck' in the

*Facing page, the town of Alleghe on the lake
of the same name.
Above, clockwise, images of the Dolomites of Belluno:
the waters of the Cordevole, which in fact divides the
western and eastern mountains, the enchanting gorge in
the Val di Piero; the mountains seen from the Passo
Durau.*

Vette Feltrine, marks the southern limit of the
Dolomites. These mountains are Dolomites to all
effects, but their lesser altitudes makes them, as
a group, less aesthetically and morphologically
important than the grandiose mountains further
north. Besides this, the mountains are difficult to
access even for expert hikers, since the trails of-

The town of Feltre in Val Belluna overlooked by the Vette Feltrine.

ten run along precipices that call for nerves of steel and an unfailing sense of balance. There are no ski trails in this area, again on account of the steepness of the slopes.

The result is a series of mountains about which little is generally known, hardly noticed by the thousands of cars that pass on their way to the other Dolomites further north. The 'poor' Dolomites, we might say - but this 'poverty' has proved to be their wealth. Isolation has permitted conservation of a truly exceptional variety of species of plants as well as of animals, which here enjoy an almost undisturbed environment.

The Parco Nazionale delle Dolomiti Bellunesi was established in 1993, and the first meeting of the board of directors was held on 22 February 1994. The surface area is about 32,000 hectares, 16,000 of which were formerly divided up among 8 nature preserves managed by the Forest Service. This park is today one of the few remaining wilderness areas in Italy - but we might ask ourselves what man would be doing in these mountains anyway. The park hosts over one thousand **chamois**, and lesser numbers of **roe deer** and

deer. Some discussion arose over the introduction of the **moufflon**, which has made itself very much, maybe even too much, at home here. But despite everything, the invertebrates remain the most important endemic species.

The park is divided into different areas, which merit being explored singly.

The Vette Feltrine. Above the city of **Feltre**, from which they take their name, these lowish peaks are the southernmost spurs of the park. The **Pavione** is the highest, at 2334 meters. The easiest route starts out from Feltre, along the road that leads to Pedavena and then to the Passo Croce d'Aunè. The **Pian d'Avena**, slightly before the pass, is an extension of meadows and woods with, among other things, an efficient equestrian center managed by the Forest Service, which for riding enthusiasts organizes four-day horseback treks through the park in a northerly direction, with overnight stays in the refuges.

A former army supply road leads from the pass to the 'Buse', high-altitude meadows that in the spring are a botanist's paradise. This is the park's most interesting area from the floristic point of view, with an incredible variety of species (almost 1000 have been registered), many of which are endemic. The floristic importance of these mountains was pointed out as early as 1742 by the great Italian botanist Zanichelli.

The Piani Eterni. These 'flats' divide the Vette Feltrine from the Monti del Sole, and despite their name offer some of the steepest slopes in the entire district. Near the **Passo dell'Olmo**, ravines, crevasses, and vertical walls are the order of the day and the excursion trails often wind along the edges of steep ravine walls - absolutely not suitable for those afraid of heights.

The **Errera plateau** is instead a vast high-altitude meadow, the summer home of hundreds of milk cows.

The most easy-to-negotiate access route is from the Valle di Canzoi, up the Caorame torrent to the **Stua** reservoir. The trail is flanked by woods of alders, birch, and willows that higher up leave room for the first Norway spruce. From the wooden bridge that crosses the torrent it is only a short distance to the Piani Eterni, a karstic sink of impressive size closed in on all sides by steep cliffs of calcareous rock.

The Parco Nazionale delle Dolomiti Bellunesi is the paradise of the chamois, a very common ani-

IN THE HIGH PASTURES

*I*n speaking of the Dolomite meadows and pastures, we often risk forgetting the animals: the bovine species most common in the Alpine summer pastures, like the **Red Pied** and the **Swiss Brown**. The Red Pied is a dual-purpose breed, neither a dairy nor a beef breed but a little of both: it does not have the same yield as the French breeds as to quality of the meat, but produces more milk, and this makes it equally competitive. The Swiss Brown is instead a typical milk breed, even though it is not as productive as the Black Pied or Friesian, which is also seen in the lower valleys. What makes the former two species preferable over others, which by now dominate in the plains areas, is their hardiness and their adaptability to high-altitude conditions.

Red Pied cows in an Alpe di Siusi pasture; below, a Swiss Brown, a typical Alpine milk breed.

CLIFFAHANGERS

The **chamois** *is a born climber, and the lightness of its stride along the long crests that would be dangerous even if taken slowly, is exhilarating. It is usually easy to spot solitary males or groups of females with their young, or even to see an adult male chasing a younger individual during the rutting season. Fights between males are very violent and terminate with the precipitous flight of the loser. The chamois are rather timid animals, but there is no need to get up close since they are easy to spot against the rock with good binoculars and because there are thousands in the area, in all the principal parks.*

mal in these mountains. It is easy to spot **chamois** on the rocky buttresses, sometimes in herds of up to 20 to 30 individuals. Good binoculars are nevertheless a necessity, since the **golden eagle** nests in these gorges, as does the **hazel hen**, the **rock ptarmigan**, and the extremely rare **eagle-owl**.

The Monti del Sole. From Belluno, take the road to Agordo (S.S. 203) through the valley cut by the Cordevole, an tributary of the **Piave** with incredibly clear waters. This itinerary is perfect for a first approach to the flora and the fauna of the park, which here is accessible even to the least expert hikers. At the 12 km milestone, on the right is the **oasis of Candaten**, near which is the Zanardo trail, a walk along which each plant is identified by an information card: a sort of living botany textbook.

To the right of the road are the Monti del Sole, the green slopes of which are home to the **Venus' slipper** (*Cypripedium calceolus*), a rare spontaneous orchid that unfortunately has become even rarer due to indiscriminate picking. In the early morning, it is easy to spot roe deer on the slopes of the Monti del Sole and **Monte Schiara**, as they timidly look out from among the trees, only to melt back into the woods at the least disturbance.

The exuberant vegetation on the steep slopes of the Monti del Sole.

FROM ALOFT

*These splendid birds are formidable hunters of marmots; for this reason, if you want to sight a **golden eagle**, remember that they fly mainly over the territories inhabited by the latter animals, and better if far away from the large summer tourist centers. One limitation is, however, set by their low numbers. One pair of golden eagle in fact requires over 10,000 hectares as hunting territory, and for this reason do not be surprised if they cross the meadow where you are laying in wait just once in a day. But neither is it unusual to spend an entire vacation in the Dolomites and see nary a one.*

From the refuge, there is a splendid view of Monte Schiara and of the 'Gusela', the steep obelisk of rock that distinguishes the Vescovà. The area is known as the Pian dei Gatt and is home to many roe deer at the edges of the woods and chamois on the ridges and cliffs. This is also one of the few places in the Dolomites where you may encounter the rare horned-nose viper (*Vipera ammodytes*).

Among the best known trails is the Alta Via delle Dolomiti No. 1.

THE VALLE DI LIVINALLONGO

The Livinallongo is the ideal continuation of the Cordevole valley, and one of the most secluded in the Dolomites. Among the valleys in the province of Bolzano it is surely

Left, the splendid golden eagle, regrettably an all-too-rare sight in the Dolomites; below, the edelweiss (Leontopodium alpinum).

The Schiara Group. This is the most important of the park's massifs. **Monte Schiara** (2563 meters), **Monte Talvena** (2541 meters), and **Monte Pelf** (2501 meters) form a single central group that overlooks all the rest.

The best access is had from the **Val Vescovà**, on the trail that from km 16 of the S.S. 203 leads, in about two hours, to the Rifugio Blanchet. The trail winds among steep limestone cliffs on which flower the rare rock rampion, the edelweiss, and the mountain lily.

FOREWARNED IS FOREARMED

*T*he three species of **vipers** present in the Dolomites are all poisonous and are considered dangerous, even though the maximum quantity of poison produced by an adult (calculated for a 100-gram mouse and certainly not for a 70-kilogram hiker) is generally insufficient to kill an adult in good health.

These vipers are in any case anything but rare. The asp viper (Vipera aspis) is in fact the most common snake in these mountains. Excursionists ought thus adopt a few elementary but essential safety precautions, such as wearing hiking boots and high woolen socks, and taking care where they sit.

The asp viper, which is rarely found above 2000 meters altitude, is gradually replaced higher up by the common adder (Vipera berus), which lives at up to 3000 meters. This snake is well adapted to both the rhododendron underwood of the fir-woods and to the screes, where it finds shelter in the mugho pine bushes.

The third species is the horned-nose viper (Vipera ammodytes), called thus for its unmistakable soft 'horn' of scales at the tip of its nose. This species is typical of the Carso and is found in the Dolomites only in certain isolated areas. This snake does not like the cold and does not live above 1500-2000 meters altitude. It is the most poisonous of the three species mentioned.

The common adder is the most common reptile in many of the Dolomite valleys. Left, the head of a horned-nose viper, the most poisonous in the area but not very common, and unmistakable thanks to the small 'horn' of scales on its nose.

that exhibiting the least Venetian influence, since it is inhabited by Ladin-speaking peoples. This Ladin territory is known locally as the 'Fodom' and was, for a long time in the past, associated with the Alto Adige in terms of culture and traditions.

The most important center is the **Pieve di Livinallongo**, with some distinctive homes and a small church in a panoramic position from which, in the late afternoon, you can see the wall of the Civetta illuminated by the declining sun.

The best-known center is instead **Arabba**, an important ski resort with some ancient homes and its 17th-century parochial church.

Above, the valley below Pieve di Livinallongo and, right, a home in Arabba.
Facing page, Monte Civetta from the Valle di Livinallongo.

On the following pages, the peak of the Lagazuoi Piccolo with its wooden crucifix. In the background, the Sorapis, the Pelmo, and the Civetta.

149

The Sella Ronda, is a true ski adventure through four passes around the Sella.

The Belvedere di Canazei lift facilities against the backdrop of the Sella.

A ski trail at Plan de Gralba, above Selva di Val Gardena.

The gentle slopes of the Pralongià upland plateau are ideal for a pleasant day on skis.

Skiing in the Dolomites unites first-class trails and fabulous landscapes.

SKIING IN THE DOLOMITES

Dolomiti Superski

The major ski district in Italy, and perhaps even in the whole world, all accessible with a single ski-pass. It includes 437 lifts in 11 valleys and 38 different ski centers, for a total of 1100 kilometers of ski trails.

If we figure that an average-to-good skier can cover, lift lines and weather permitting, a maximum of about 50 kilometers per day, it would take three whole weeks to try all the trails in the district. It is thus no wonder that skiers who have been skiing the Dolomites for decades still succeed in discovering new trails.

However, the greatest advantage of Dolomiti Superski is not so much the number of trails as the fact that most of them are linked, and thus, theoretically, it would be possible to put on your skis and spend an entire week in the mountains without ever taking them off. All with no limitations on ski-passes, back and forth on skis among the provinces of Bolzano, Trento, and Belluno. The principal ski district centers on Monte Sella, which you can round in either direction on the Sella Ronda, and ranges from Ortisei to the west to Canazei to the south and San Cassiano to the east as far as the Passo del Falzarego.

Although these trails are connected, in practice one would have to be a champion skier to succeed in starting from San Cassiano and reaching Arabba, then Canazei, then over the Passo Sella to Selva and from there to Ortisei and to the Alpe di Siusi (and then, of

The head of the Boè trail, in the Val Badia, in the magical light of dawn.

course, returning to San Cassiano) in a single day. Even with no lines at the lifts, the distance and the time required to ski down and then ride back up make this ideal circle an impossible dream.

Although other districts, like Cortina, are included on the same ski-pass, they are actually self-sufficient 'islands'.

Ski Districts, Centers, and Trails

THE SELLA RONDA
This circuit around the Sella permits the skier to perform the unique exploit of skiing around a mountain over 3000 meters high, crossing four different passes on the way: the Pordoi, the Sella, the Gardena, and the Campolongo. The course is also known as the Giro dei Quattro Passi (Four Passes). The time required, with no lines at the lifts, goes from 4 hours for experts to 6 for average skiers. This course is not recommended for beginners.

The Sella Ronda can be skied in either direction, but the counterclockwise itinerary, which was also the first to be fully linked up, is far and away the most beautiful. Among the places of note along the way are the Città dei Sassi, under the Sassolungo group, where you have to pole to get over the rises but which smacks of adventure; the 'superhighway', the long, monotonous trail that from Canazei takes you to Arabba; the final

stretch of the Boè trail; and the splendid trails that lead to Selva di Val Gardena. The clockwise itinerary is suitable even for less accomplished skiers, but is less suggestive. The descent from the Passo Gardena to Corvara is fun, with an interminable series of trails, but the ascent from Arabba to Canazei, with another interminable series of lifts, is tedious. But in either direction, this is one of the world's most beautiful ski excursions.

ALPE DI SIUSI
Dominating Ortisei, this broad plateau boasts many trails. Theoretically, it is linked to all the others, but in practice it is decentralized with respect to the heart of the Dolomiti Superski district, and so much so that it is difficult to ascend the Alpe from Ortisei and then head for Selva without losing a lot of time in conveyance. The Alpe di Siusi, nevertheless, is more than enough for a day on skis. There are many easy trails, and it is therefore perfect for beginners or families with children.

BELVEDERE DI CANAZEI
A vast upland plain where on paper there are a great many trails but in truth only a single, immense one. This is the ideal spot for beginners, since there are no forced curves and if you lose control of your skis it is practically impossible to end up off the trail. The link with the Sella Ronda

and with the beautiful ski district of the nearby Campitello di Fassa is interesting; the trails on the other side that form the first stretch of the descents toward Arabba are more stimulating than the Belvedere proper.

COL RODELLA
Col Rodella is reached through Campitello di Fassa; it is a small ski district included in the great circuit of the Sella. The view from the Sassolungo is awesome, and the trails are comme il faut.

SANTA CRISTINA IN VAL GARDENA
The Santa Cristina ski district extends into the central area of the valley, with the northern trails pushing somewhat impudently into the Parco delle Odle. What is more, with their southern exposure they are also frequently without snow cover. This district is important mostly because it links the Alpe di Siusi with the Selva ski trails.

The southern side of the valley, instead, is in shadow and thus offers better snow conditions. It is here that we find the spectacular trail, with its frequent changes in slope, on which the 'Libera di Santa Cristina' World Cup downhill race is held. As you ski the trail as a tourist, it's fun to imagine the professionals, who descend at over 120 kilometers/hour!

Excellent lift facilities abound throughout the Dolomites.

The Val Badia seen from the La Villa ski trails.

Facilities at Grostè in the Madonna di Campiglio ski area.

The start of a ski trail at Ra Valles.

Panorama from the Lagazuoi Piccolo over the Col Gallina trails at the Passo del Falzarego.

A view of the Alleghe ski area.

A new lift facility at Alleghe's Prà della Crosta.

SELVA DI VAL GARDENA

This ski district is also divided into two areas, since on one side are found the Danterciepies, long and truly beautiful ski trails that link the Passo Gardena with the town; on the other, a vast district with shorter trails that are, however, suitable for all 'legs' and skill levels. Both slopes are integral parts of the Giro dei Quattro Passi.

BOÈ

This is a single trail which merits separate treatment, since its setting is particularly fortunate. It starts from the beginning of the upper tract of the Vallon and runs its whole length, and is in the opinion of many skiers the most beautiful trail in the Dolomites. The point of departure is on the crest, where it feels like you're skiing in the sky: broad curves on an extremely smooth bottom down a steep but uniform slope make it the best a skier who knows how to lift his eyes from the snow could ever hope for.

The Boè is the Corvara trail that with the nearby Colfosco and Selva di Val Gardena represent what we might call a nerve center. From here it is possible to reach every locality on this great roundabout of trails and to return to your starting point, all in the same day.

A place to discover: a small group of three trails just above Colfosco, which are all but invisible from below.

PRALONGIÀ

Like the Belvedere di Canazei and the Alpe di Siusi, this is for those who want to change trails often without stray-

Skiers relaxing on the Grosté.

ing too far from home base and their hotel in the evening.

Pralongià is famous for its kilometers-long trails at every skill level that descend from both the north side (La Villa and San Cassiano) and the south (Corvara). An easy trail, starting out from Prati di Ruones, lands you in Corvara after about seven kilometers of pleasant skiing through woods and gentle upland plateaus. The Pralongià is idyllic for safe off-the-trail skiing.

LA VILLA

There are two trails worthy of note at La Villa: the red trail, which is second only to Boè as to beauty, and the famous black trail, better known as the Gran Risa. This is a World Cup trail, and just looking at it gives you the shivers. It is an excellent black, one of those that demands all the skier's prowess, and is obviously suitable only for real experts. A sort of baptism by fire - or by ice.

THE PORTA VESCOVO

This is the ski district of Arabba and the milieu of accomplished skiers. Always in shadow, it is not ideal for those looking for a high-altitude tan, but the exposure keeps the trails in excellent condition even in the spring, when in many other places the snow has already begun to loosen in the heat. The red trails are simply marvelous, while the blues

are fickle and since they are narrow and on reverse gradients end up being more difficult than the reds.

The blacks are true blacks, not to be underestimated. From Porta Vescovo, instead of descending toward Arabba, you may choose the opposite direction and take a leisurely jaunt on skis through the woods to Malga Ciapela. There are, however, two obstacles: the glacier is open only in the summer, or in any case when the trails that lead here have already become flowered meadows, and the Marmolada lift facilities, although they are linked, are not part of Dolomiti Superski and there is a separate charge.

Other Ski Districts

There are many areas scattered here and there in the various valleys that are in excellent positions but too isolated to be linked with any ease to the other districts. In such cases, the alternatives are using your own car or the ski-buses that run up and down the valleys.

The service is frequent, the buses have ski racks, and they permit the residents of the areas that lie outside the major ski districts (for example, the first towns in the Val di Fassa, like Moneta, Vigo, Pozza, and Pera) to avoid using their own means for moving around. The ski-bus ticket is included in the ski-pass.

THE FALZAREGO TRAIL

More than a ski trail, this is an excursion for the afficionados of the mountains. It is included in Dolomiti Superski and is in a certain sense linked to it, since it is possible to descend from Pralongià to Armentarola and from there take the bus to the Passo di Falzarego. The trail descends through a spectacular gorge with sheer walls and enormous frozen waterfalls. Although it is not much as a trail, the scenery is spectacular. The only jarring note is the last flat

The lift facilities linking Pescul and Alleghe, at Selva di Cadore.

Off-the-trail skiing on the Marmolada glacier with the Piz Boè in the background.

View of a lift facility that cuts across a ski trail at Borca di Cadore.

The Pralongià trails offer a lovely panorama of Corvara and the Sassongher.

A stretch of the wide red trail at Palafavera in the Val Zoldana.

stretch of some kilometers, along which you must pole like a cross.-country skier. There is a sporadic sled service that pulls skiers to the end of the trail, for a separate fee. You are thus back in Armentarola and the Pralongià group.

THE TRAILS OF CORTINA

The pearl of the Dolomites offers beautiful trails that are unfortunately divided up between two districts and very far removed from the main circuit, of which they would be part but for the fact that it can be reached only by road,

over the Passo del Falzarego. Of the two districts, that which faces the Cristallo group is less interesting, but most suitable for beginners. The Tofane district, instead, has a sufficient number of trails and some very beautiful ones, for skiers of every skill level. The first stretch of the black trail is quite difficult. The ski-and-climb combinations proposed by the local tourist offices are also quite interesting.

VALLE DI SAN PELLEGRINO

This area is divided into two districts: the Alpe di Lusia, which has very long, good trails and links up with the Ballamonte on the opposite side, and the more important San Pellegrino - Passo Valles - Falcade ski district. The few trails from the Passo di San Pellegrino are valorized by the link with the more numerous trails of Falcade at the end of the same valley.

SAN MARTINO DI CASTROZZA AND PASSO ROLLE

Like in the Valle di San Pellegrino valley, there are two distinct districts here: the San Martino di Castrozza trails, some of which are extremely long, and the adjacent but unlinked Passo Rolle trails.

THE LATEMAR TRAILS

This ski district winds through the area above Predazzo and in a part of the other side of the mas-

sif around the Passo di Costalunga - but there the trails are rather short. The Predazzo trails, instead, are many and varied. A series of 'chained' trails takes you away from the town and almost completely around the Latemar to San Floriano.

THE CIVETTA SKI DISTRICT

This particularly beautiful and interesting area would merit being more famous than it is. Eighty kilometers of trails and a lower ski-pass price with respect to Dolomiti Superski, in which it is not included. It is quite crowded on weekends but empty enough the other days of the week due to the lack of mass tourist accommodations in the Val di Zoldo. Only Alleghe has a larger number of hotels. The district unites Alleghe with the Val di Zoldo and runs around the impressive Civetta massif, with excellent cross-country trails and slopes that all things considered are universally accessible. Pecol has a black trail that is, however, not all that difficult. Many beginners consider themselves real skiers after having skied it a few times - but then when they try some of the other black trails, such as the Porta Vescovo or the Gran Risa, they often reappraise their skill level. The trails that descend to Pescul are lovely, the red Palafavera trail is wide, and the red trail that descends to Alleghe, besides having a

pleasant slope, offers a panoramic view over the frozen lake.

THE BRENTA DOLOMITES

Madonna di Campiglio is coveted by skiers at least as much as is Cortina on the opposite side of the group. The trails are satisfactory even though, to tell the truth, the heart of the ski district is higher up, at Campo Carlo Magno. From here you can head either toward the Grosté or toward Marilleva or Folgarida. The Grosté is a vast sloping plain with trails that start at 2500 meters, where there is almost always snow even when the temperatures lower down are higher. The trails of Madonna di Campiglio that depart from the Spinale are on the whole less attractive than those that descend to Campo Carlo Magno. But since they are linked, this is not a great problem. The well-kept Marilleva and Folgarida trails are good skiing on pleasant slopes. The problem with these towns, however, is that their tourist accommodation capacity is high in proportion to the number of trails. The result is that in the high season there are always lines at the lifts. This is a splendid ski district, but it shows its best face during the low season.

THE SADDLES AND EXTREME SKIING

For thrill-seekers, there are the extreme ski trails, like the saddles of the

Sassolungo or the Sella. The gradient is formidable in all cases, and the danger is real, because if you fall once you are likely to wind up among the rocks, and fatal accidents have already occurred. It is therefore a good idea to take advantage of the local guide services that organize Alpine ski excursions, and remember: skiing at extreme levels calls for good legs, but also nerves of steel.

A typical descent is that of the Val di Mesdì, in a breathtaking gorge that cuts the Sella in half. This is a real adventure, and is suitable only for extremely expert skiers. The Corvara and Colfosco ski schools organize group excursions, taking into account the weather conditions and the danger of avalanches. For those who so desire, there are also organized excursions in which the ascent can be made by helicopter.

Cross-Country Skiing

The most important and best known of the cross-country ski ring is the 'Marcialonga' itinerary, a true marathon route that links Cavalese, in Val di Fiemme, with Alba di Canazei, at the extremity of the Val di Fassa, and more than enough even for the most powerful and long-winded athletes.

Other rings are scattered throughout almost all of the valleys, but to cite some here would only be an injustice to those we leave out.

An extraordinary slope at the Cinque Torri under the looming Tofana di Rozes.

On the following pages, Monte Civetta from the Zoldo side.

Cross-country skiing is another popular sport in the Dolomites.

INDEX